PRIMARY
PROFESSIONAL BOOKSHELF

TEACHING NUMERACY

maths in the primary classroom

EDITED BY RUTH MERTTENS

Published by Scholastic Ltd
Villiers House
Clarendon Avenue
Leamington Spa
Warwickshire CV32 5PR

Authors Ruth Merttens,
Helen Williams, Laurie Rousham, Tim Rowland,
Tony Brown, Valerie Emblen, Sheila Ebbutt.
General Editor Ruth Merttens
Desk Editor Joel Lane
Series Designer Lynne Joesbury
Designer Lynda Murray

Designed using Aldus Pagemaker
Printed in Great Britain by Bell & Bain Ltd, Glasgow

British Library Cataloguing-in-Publication Data
A catalogue record for this book is available from the British Library.

ISBN 0-590-53429-7

PRIMARY
PROFESSIONAL BOOKSHELF

CONTENTS

ACKNOWLEDGEMENTS
Thanks to:
David Fulton Publishers for the use of an extract from
Mathematics in the Primary School: A Sense of Progression
© 1996 C. Hopkins *et al* (1996, David Fulton Publishers)
Cambridge University Press for the use of an extract from
Cambridge Primary Mathematics: Talking Points in Maths by Anita Straker
© 1993 Anita Straker (1993, CUP)
SCAA for the use of an extract from *Consistency in Teacher Assessment*
© Crown Copyright (1995, HMSO)

FOREWORD

This book addresses all those who are interested in the teaching and learning of numerical skills. It sets out to provide some answers to the following questions:

✧ How is it that some children become fluent in numeracy, while others continue to struggle with basic concepts and techniques?

✧ What can teachers do to enable children to develop that all-important 'sense of number'?

✧ What is the relationship between written and mental work in numeracy, and how do we foster a facility with and a confidence in both?

✧ How do we pitch our teaching so as to take account of what children bring to the classroom in terms of previous numerical experience and knowledge?

The great strength of a book which has contributions from many different authors is that each one brings her or his own perspective and experience to the attempt to answer these questions. In this case, each of the authors certainly has a unique and particular expertise; but there is nevertheless a commonality in their approaches, with a focus on the development of appropriate pedagogical strategies.

As editor, I must pay tribute to the professionalism and efficiency of the contributors. But even with excellent co-authors, in a book like this it is essential to draw upon the experiences and advice of those with whom one is working at the time of writing. With this in mind, I must acknowledge all the help I have had from Dave Kirkby, with whom I have had so many long and intricate arguments about the nature of children's learning in numeracy, who has consistently forced me to address those troublesome details which interfere with a good theory, and who never lets me get away with an unproven assertion. I must acknowledge my family. It goes without saying that the production of any book interferes to an unpardonable extent with family life, and my younger sons Matthew and Wilf and my husband Ian have provided me with love, cups of tea, and examples of mathematical learning in equal measure. However, I would like to dedicate this book to Mike O'Regan, Sinéad, Sarah and all the teachers on the Hamilton Mathematics Project, whose commitment to raising children's achievement in numeracy is a constant source of inspiration.

CHAPTER 1

INTRODUCTION

PRIMARY MATHS IN CRISIS: WHAT IS TO BE DONE?

For those of us involved in mathematics education, it sometimes feels as if every time we open a newspaper or listen to the news, we encounter yet another complaint about maths standards. Even allowing for the tendency of reporters to exaggerate and to look for the most gloomy prognosis, things do not look encouraging. Many teachers are asking questions about the best ways in which they can teach maths in a situation of rising class sizes and ever-decreasing resources.

In this book, we explore a variety of perspectives on the teaching and learning of numeracy. Each of the authors, in her or his own way, and within the context of her or his own particular topic, tries to suggest a way forward, and (with reference to both theory and practice) envisages some realistic and concrete possibilities for raising the standard of what is achieved by the children and teachers in primary classrooms. Although each chapter takes a different view of the theme and addresses its own specific concerns, there is a common thread running through the book. All of the chapters emphasise a need for teachers to think about the more formal aspects of numeracy, especially in relation to some searching questions about some of the more 'child-centred' or 'discovery-learning' approaches prevalent in the late 1970s and the 1980s. Similarly, all the authors manifest a feeling that we have consistently downplayed those aspects of teaching concerned with the provision of specific strategies and techniques, and emphasised those aspects of teaching concerned with investigational mathematics. While we continue to agree that both are important, there is a general agreement here that we need to tilt the balance away from the latter emphasis and towards the former.

In order to work towards a reassessment of our own teaching

approaches and techniques in maths education, I think it is helpful to elaborate a model for classroom practice in primary mathematics. Any model is only (at best) a heuristic device to enable us to frame a general analysis of the problems, difficulties and possible solutions, and any model 'creaks' if you push it too far or too hard. Nonetheless an effective model can enable us to create a vision of what might be, and a shared analysis of what is. The following model is thus presented in the spirit of this book – to afford ways of looking and speaking which enable us to go forward in our thinking and our practice, and to constrain both excessive criticism and unfounded assertion.

TEACHING

The model of classroom practice which we wish to share begins with something called 'teaching'. This is perhaps the aspect of classroom activity which has been most neglected over the past twenty years. Teachers have been encouraged to construe their role as that of facilitators or enablers in contrast to their traditional role as instructors. Two factors in the 1960s acted to transform primary education in this regard: the influence of the developmental model of learning associated with Piaget, and the advent of individualised workbooks.

Piagetian arguments emanating from the Plowden Report and heavily reinforced from across the Atlantic pushed teachers into a situation where they virtually stopped 'teaching' maths. The prevalent styles of the 1950s and 1960s – characteristically the group teaching techniques of the infant schools and the class teaching styles of the junior schools – were gradually displaced by a fundamentally different approach. All over Britain, mathematics lessons ceased to exist in the form that had lasted for two generations. Taught lessons were replaced by individualised learning regimes.

The educational argument for this change is easy to summarise. Children learn at different rates. Individual workbooks and textbooks allow children to work through the mathematics syllabus at their own rate. Those who need to can work fast; those who need more time can work slowly. The teacher can structure her or his time so as to work with individual children if and when they need assistance.

This educational argument was driven, to some extent, by pressure from publishers and educationalists involved in the production of educational learning systems. It was also driven by an individualist ideology whose basis – though politically diverse – was a reaction against the authoritarian character of traditional 'schooling'.

However, a major effect of these changes was that children's efforts in mathematics were centred on tackling the problems emanating from the printed page. Concomitant and predictable difficulties arose from the problems of the inarticulate or muddled author, the inadequate diagram, the ambiguous text – in short, this was a rigid structure which failed to give sufficient support to those who were struggling, and at the same time confused or restrained those who needed to move on to new ideas. The classroom became a silent place, where queues of children waited to see the teacher when they had a 'problem'. Teachers could not easily discuss central topics because the children were scattered across the length and breadth of the curriculum and there was no mathematical core to the lessons. Most importantly, children could not talk to each other, or give each other advice, explanation or help, because they were all at different levels and on different topics. The result was that many children had no confidence and little practice in articulating problems, discussing solutions or explicating their ideas.

Yet, as Tony Brown succinctly puts it, 'Children were, and are, desperate to be taught, to receive explanations and to have a dialogue about their work both with their peers and with their teacher.'[1] Teachers are able, and increasingly are being encouraged, to provide more 'up-front' teaching of central mathematical concepts. Many teachers recognise the need to offer children strategies and techniques which enable them to perform specific operations, and then to encourage the children to adapt or move on from these strategies and to invent their own, modified techniques. So what do we understand by the verb *to teach*? We know that teaching is both an active and a skilled process. We recognise that it is an art, not a science. What are we doing when we 'teach' a group of children?

Teaching, I believe, may be characterised under five aspects – not all of which will be present in any one instance of teaching, but all of which are necessarily part of what it is to teach. Firstly, teachers *instruct*. They often provide a series of instructions: a procedure (oral or written) to enable children to carry out a task. 'Fourteen add four. Hold the first number in your head [hand on head to 'hold' it in] and then count on using the fingers of your other hand – fifteen, sixteen, seventeen, eighteen.' The child has a method, a way of doing something. Later they may adapt this method, transform it or even replace it entirely with a better method of their own. But for now, they can perform the required operation and thus build their confidence and proficiency.

Secondly, teachers *model* things. They demonstrate how to do something and thus show children that it is both possible and (hopefully) enjoyable. Teachers model what it is to 'be a mathematician', and also what it is to do a particular piece of maths. When the teacher shows children how to count in twos by holding up one finger for each number spoken, pausing to show the numbers of fingers standing (for example, five) and saying 'Five twos are ten', she or he is demonstrating a skill or technique. This demonstration, which always has a dramatic or 'performance' element in it, enables children to engage with the performance, to interpret it as a strategy, and to utilise it for their own purposes.

Thirdly, teachers *explain* things to children. As the quote from Tony Brown suggests, children are desperate to receive explanations and to offer their own. Teachers say, 'This happens because...' or 'That's because this isn't a one, but a ten...'. They suggest new ways of looking at something. They offer not only specific accounts, but a whole way of talking, so that the children can develop their own accounts of why something happens. Without the teacher's explanations, very little makes sense in maths – and worse, the children lack an appropriate language for constructing mathematical explanations. They cannot even put their ideas into words, because they do not have access to a vocabulary for this purpose.

Fourthly, teachers *question* children (and themselves). Questioning is an extremely powerful technique, whereby teachers direct children's attention to the salient parts of the problem. In this context the 'tone' is crucial. Children who have been part of a classroom where it is acceptable to ask as well as answer questions, to give a 'wrong' answer and have it valued and discussed seriously, and to not know an answer, develop an enthusiastic and considered response to the whole process of question and answer. Questioning can be a threatening and intimidating tactic, or it can be a liberating and stimulating one; the difference lies in the tone adopted by the teacher, and the familiarity of the children with the approach. Children who have never been questioned, or who have never had to answer questions in public, may find it threatening; but those who are used to the back-and-forth exchange of teachers' questions and children's suggested answers, where incorrect answers as well as correct ones are being valued for the discussion and the learning they produce, will have no such fears.

Finally, teachers *narrate*. They take pains to locate the mathematics within a narrative context, so that it makes sense to the children. As Martin Hughes observed in *Children and Number* (1986), children can answer questions in context which they cannot answer in abstract. ('What is two and one more?' 'Dunno.' 'Well, what is two elephants and one more elephant?' 'Three elephants'.[2]) As teachers, we often provide a 'story' context without even noticing that we are doing so. 'Well, you've got 20p pocket money, and your Mum says she'll double it. How much have you got now?' The short narrative context does more than simply contextualise the maths: it provides a rationale for doing it and wanting to get it right.

Teaching thus seems to me to be at the heart of primary mathematics in the classroom. Against the tendency of the last twenty years, we can assert the importance of active teaching; and we need to look for the skills we have to develop in this vein and the support structures which need to be in place for this to happen. It is equally important to state that, against the grain of some current arguments in favour of a return to traditional teaching methods, *teaching is not telling*. Lining up children and telling them things did not work in the past. It does not work today in those countries which rely upon very didactic methods, and it will certainly not work in the future. Teaching is an interactive process. It is *dialogue*, and it assumes and is predicated upon a notion of good dialogue, with an element of dramatic performance. Children need to have conversations with their teacher, in the context of a large group or a whole-class lesson where the children's own contributions to discussion are part of the teaching and learning process.

MAKING SENSE

Children need to make sense of the mathematics we teach them. There is no point in our doing all this wonderful and enthusiastic teaching if the children do not take what we have taught them and make it their own. Much attention has been given by researchers and practitioners to how children best assimilate, accommodate, transform and transfer the mathematics of the classroom. Throughout the 1960s, 1970s and 1980s, it was generally assumed that children made sense of their maths by being able to realise the operation *in concrete terms*. Thus we witnessed a tremendous move towards practical activities (what in North America are called 'manipulatives') meant to enable children to 'do' their mathematics as a practical and physical subject. And certainly, it cannot be denied that children often make sense of a mathematical operation or idea by being able to move blocks around, count marbles, or use base ten equipment. Many of the mathematical activities provided by maths schemes or suggested by other commercial materials have this concrete realisation as their basis.

However, we are now more aware that practical activities are not the only way in which children come to make sense of the maths they do. Images and metaphors play an important role. The image of the number line (that is, of numbers as positions on a line or in a series) is one of the most crucial images for young children learning mathematics. It is worth reflecting how much time we spend in the nursery and reception matching numbers to quantities of things, and how important the number line is by comparison. Hilary Shuard used to say that the most important progression in learning mathematics was from counting to counting *on*. It is impossible for children to progress from counting if they have no mental model of the number system to draw upon.

Looked at in one light, all four operations (addition, subtraction, multiplication and division), involve counting on in one way or another. Addition is counting on, first in ones, then in tens and ones, then to the next ten or the next hundred. Subtraction can best be construed as counting on from one thing to another. Thus 45 – 29 is how many we need to count on from 29 to get to 45. This counting on strategy is easily the most helpful in terms of providing a mental rather than a written procedure (see Chapter 5). Multiplication is counting on in groups of two, three and so on. Division can be characterised as counting how many sets are in a particular number (for example, how many threes are in 21?).

Given how important the number line is as a mental model, it is vital that teachers provide children with examples of this image – from a washing line with big numbers pegged along it to small personal number lines which children keep in their books or at their desks to help them count. Other images which are essential in helping children to make sense of their maths include the 0–99 number grid, where the direction of movement helps children to understand what happens when we add ten or take away one. Fingers are also important images when used in a symbolic capacity – that is, where each finger 'stands for' something (for example, each finger stands for ten or two as we count in tens or twos).

Children also make sense of maths through games and puzzles. As they play a number game or work out how a particular trick works, they explore the nature of the operations they are using and the results obtained. For example, the famous cracker trick where I can tell you what number you are thinking of if you tell me which lists of numbers it is in relies upon the fact that any number can be produced by adding a combination of the binary numbers (1, 2, 4, 8, 16 etc). This is not only a trick which children enjoy playing and which improves their mental addition, it is also a stimulus for thinking about how our number system works. Games and tricks allow children to practise their numerical skills in a context where it is important for them not to make a mistake. This directly encourages children to check their own work and to estimate, both things which it is hard to persuade them to do in other contexts.

All the above-mentioned ways in which children come to make sense of the maths they are learning have one thing in common. They all involve *talk*. Children need to talk things through. Plato defined learning as dialogue, and thought as the inner dialogue of the soul with itself; it can be argued that we cannot improve on these definitions. As children manipulate bricks or counters, count along the number line or play a mathematical game, they talk about the maths involved. They struggle to express what they are thinking and to use speech to help them remember what to do and what the results are. The importance of talk in both the teaching and the learning of mathematics cannot be exaggerated. Unless mathematics is talked through, and articulacy striven for, the child's mental structure of mathematical ideas remains loose, incomplete, disconnected and inarticulate (both in the sense of not being linked or hinged and in the sense of not flowing).

PRACTICE

The third part of the process we are describing may be characterised as practising the skills that have been taught. Children need not only to make sense of the maths, they need to practise it. As with teaching, practice and repetition have had a slightly bad name over the last twenty years. The implication that children were 'rote learning' something or were being fed on a diet of 'drill and practice' was enough to send most teachers scurrying to their local maths centre for professional advice and support. There has been a great reduction in the amount of oral repetitive work and mental (also oral) practice in maths over the last twenty-five years. This has come about partly as a consequence of the switch to an individualised workbook regime, since it is almost impossible to use memorisation and repetition as class or whole-group activities when thirty children are working through thirty different pieces of text. It has become a useful argument to suggest that memorisation, ritual chanting and oral mathematics were not helpful, and that is why we no longer do them. This argument contains an element of post-hoc justification.

There are two reasons for practising a skill. The first concerns the necessity of allowing particular skills to become automatic. We need children to become sufficiently familiar with certain mathematical routines and operations that they no longer have to decide what to do: they perform them without thinking. There is a parallel here with a skill such as driving a car or riding a bike. If children simply 'know' that four more added to 26 makes 30, they have a great advantage over those who have to work this out every time by counting on. Similarly, those who can add ten or multiples of ten with an automaticity born of complete familiarity have a head start in performing some of the more complex mental algorithms. The issue of practice and repetition is raised in the context of allowing skills to become 'automatised' in Chapters 2, 3 and 5.

The second reason for practising a skill is that it assists the memorisation process. Children not only need to remember number facts such as multiplication tables and bonds to ten, twenty, one hundred and so on, they also need to memorise particular procedures and operations. Part of this process of memorising involves the development of a real familiarity with the subject. Familiarity is essential for developing children's confidence and capability. Learning *by rote* has become a byword for bad practice; but in adopting this view, we have seemed to forget that there can also be learning *by heart*. The difference is one between learning things purely in order to recite them and learning things in order to use and apply them. Oral repetition, listening and joining in with others as they learn the same things, and being helped and tested by teachers or parents are all useful means by which children can become familiar with aspects of maths.

READING THIS BOOK

How can we read this book in the light of the model of classroom practice discussed above? Each of the chapters which follow deals with an aspect of developing numeracy in the primary classroom. The second chapter addresses the key questions and issues for those who are working with very young children in the nursery, reception and lower infant school. As we have suggested in elaborating the model of 'teach, make sense, practise', it is important to look at alternatives to the prevailing, somewhat limited view of the ways in which children come to make sense of numbers. Helen Williams uses her own and others' research to describe how children use numbers and how they describe what they are doing. Drawing on first-hand observations and transcripts of children's conversation, she discusses the ways in which teachers can use children's existing knowledge to advance their numerical thinking. Her chapter has important practical implications for the ways in which teachers approach number work with young children. The emphasis in this chapter is on the mental and linguistic aspects of the development of what we might call numerical 'fluency' in children.

The third chapter focuses more on the ways in which we describe the teaching and learning of maths. Taking a historical perspective, the chapter charts the development of particular ideas about how children learn and the related pedagogical approaches. It then moves on to consider new ways of construing what we do when we teach maths. Instruction and demonstration in teaching are considered as part of an approach which attempts to foreground the teaching of particular strategies and techniques. There is a sustained attempt, in this chapter, to shift the focus of attention from how well children may be said to 'understand' the maths they are doing to whether they can provide what we call a 'reading' of the mathematical statements or sentences in front of them. Thus we move from asking 'How well do you understand this?' to asking 'Can you tell me what this says/ what that means?' The view being expressed here is that children learn maths very much as they learn language, through *using* it. It follows that the *meaning* of a mathematical expression is established for children as they use it.

The fourth chapter returns to a perennial issue of importance in primary mathematics: the use of calculators. Taking a historical perspective again, we can see how, following the implementation of the PrIME project,[3] teachers were encouraged and even exhorted to use calculators as an important part of their teaching of maths. However, an equally strong movement in the opposite direction is currently gathering momentum, with suggestions that British children have been disadvantaged in comparison with their European counterparts by an over-reliance on calculators.[4] Sorting out fact from fiction and truth from opinion is more than usually difficult for teachers in this area, compressed as they are between the demands of an over-ambitious curriculum and a real concern over falling standards. Laurie Rousham and Tim Rowland take us through some of the arguments, discussing them in relation to current research. They draw upon their own work, as well as that of others in the field, to make some pragmatic recommendations.

The fifth chapter returns to a discussion of how to teach numeracy, with a focus upon algorithms. The authors use the definition of an algorithm as 'a rule for solving a mathematical problem in a finite number of steps', which allows them to consider both mental and written procedures and the essential relationship between the two. The difficulties which children have in performing algorithms are described in some detail, and the authors use this analysis to help them formulate some pragmatic algorithms. They work through some examples of the variety of different algorithms, both mental and written, which can be suggested by teachers and used by children in order to help them achieve fluency and confidence in number operations. The mental models which underpin these different algorithms are considered, and the ways in which teachers can produce these in their teaching and help children to develop them are discussed.

The sixh chapter addresses the crucial issue of the content of primary mathematics in relation to language and culture. Valerie Emblen draws upon her own research over a number of years to provide an analysis of the ways in which bilingual children have to operate within a monolingual mathematics classroom. She uses her research and experiences to make some insightful and practical suggestions about how teachers can make the most of the cultural and linguistic assets of the multilingual, multicultural classroom. Reading this chapter forces a recognition of the effects not only of the mathematical disadvantage which has dogged some of these children, but also of the endemic social and economic disadvantage within which too many of their families are embedded. A full awareness of the social context within which these children operate, where the effects of racism are all too often visible, increases the urgency of the need to welcome, respect and value the languages and cultural practices that these children have to offer the mathematics teacher.

Chapter 7 explores the notion of play in the teaching and learning of mathematics. This is a discursive chapter, in which a broad view is provided of what it means to include play in the teaching of mathematics. The relation of play to children's cognitive development is discussed, as well as its relation to their affective and social development. Tony Brown also takes an historical view of at how different cultures have incorporated various 'playful' techniques into their mathematical development, and how these have had a structural role in the development of mathematics itself. He draws upon and describes a variety of different techniques for performing arithmetic operations, including the use of fingers and counting devices such as the abacus. This fascinating account of the genesis of some of our ways of counting and doing mathematics provides the backdrop for some pragmatic suggestions and analyses of classroom techniques. In this chapter, Tony Brown also foregrounds the role of the teacher as an active instructor, leading the class through playful but structured number activities.

Chapter 8 takes us through the whole question of assessing mathematics in a classroom context. Sheila Ebbutt draws upon a wealth of experience as Director of the BEAM (Be a Mathematician) team in London to provide a clear and comprehensive account of the place of assessment within the primary maths curriculum. The chapter is rich in factual examples, and is of great practical use to teachers concerned with discovering and providing evidence of what children can and cannot do in mathematics. The chapter starts with a discussion of some of the issues involved in assessment, and takes us through an analysis of the different types of assessment and their purposes. Sheila Ebbutt also provides her readers with extremely useful references to the resources needed at each stage of her suggested programmes of assessment.

We began this introduction with a reminder that primary maths is currently in a state of flux. Looking at it positively, this provides all those concerned with the teaching of mathematics to primary and nursery-aged children with an opportunity to reflect upon some of the 'taken-for-granted' ideas and practices of the last ten or twenty years in primary education. We can re-evaluate not only our ways of doing things, but also the explanations we give and the accounts we supply in order to justify what we do. I think this is both an exciting and a challenging time to be a teacher in a primary or nursery school. This book reflects the excitement and engages with the challenge.

NOTES

1. Unpublished notes, Tony Brown, 1996.
2. *Children and Number* (1986), page 48.
3. The PrIME Project was based at Homerton College, Cambridge, under the direction of Hilary Shuard, in the second half of the 1980s. It had a national network of participating authorities.
4. See Sig Prais in 'Improving School Mathematics in Practice', paper given at the Gatsby Seminar in London (February 1995).

CHAPTER 2

DEVELOPING NUMERACY IN THE EARLY YEARS

INTRODUCTION

> 'When we were little children we had tremendous mental powers, and we still treat them as if they had none.'
>
> *Caleb Gattegno speaking to the conference of the Association of Teachers of Mathematics, April 1988*

For some years there has been an increasing body of research illustrating young children's possession of many and complex abilities (Aubrey, 1994; Bruner, 1960, 1975; Donaldson, 1978; Gattegno, 1981; Hughes, 1982, 1986; Merttens and Newland, 1996; Tizard and Hughes, 1984), and the influence of context in allowing young children (and probably all of us) access to mathematical problems (Donaldson, 1978; Walkerdine, 1988). This research challenges the writings of Jean Piaget, whose work largely underpins primary education in Great Britain. Particularly relevant to early years mathematics education are Piaget's two contentions: firstly that a child under the age of seven is incapable of logical, abstract thought; and secondly that learning is subordinate to cognitive development. For Piaget, the onus is on the child to learn, rather than on the teacher to teach.[1]

The theoretical basis of this chapter is as follows:

✧ Firstly, all children arrive at school with a considerable range and depth of knowledge about number. I will be arguing in this chapter for an early years approach that builds on these experiences and pieces of knowledge, combining them with the more formal and contrived environment of the classroom without confining children to one way of performing.

✧ Secondly, children have ways of thinking that are different from those of adults. These are complex, but often immature. Mathematical thinking develops when a child's thinking is nurtured, matured and further structured through interaction with peers and adults. In this chapter, I will be discussing the fundamental role of the teacher in the early learning process.

WHAT'S WRONG WITH SORTING AND MATCHING?

Parent and child after first day of school:

> P: What did you do today?
>
> C: Well, I spent a long time sorting out Mrs Williams' animals, but when I finished, she tipped them all back in the box.

For some years, children's early mathematics diet has consisted largely of sorting, matching and subsequent colouring. Why?

Firstly, Piaget's theory of early learning had its basis in the belief that there are universal stages in human cognitive development. He argued that children pass through recognisable stages, from the primitive to the sophisticated. Each stage is dependent on the previous one, and each prescribes what particular areas of knowledge and understanding a child is ready to develop. Presenting children with experiences appropriate to a later developmental stage is thus seen as futile.

Secondly, for Piaget, the origin of mathematics lies in the actions that the child performs on objects: every thought must have been, at some stage in the individual's past, an action. Thus the learning of numeracy has to start with concrete objects.

Consider Piaget's beliefs in relation to young children learning about number. Children under seven are seen by Piaget as 'primitive' thinkers incapable of abstract thought, able to perform certain mathematical operations only when these are embodied in physical actions on concrete objects. However, numbers are abstract, and being numerate requires us to 'work in our heads'. Young children's numeracy depends on co-ordinating the act of counting, a complex process, with the knowledge that number has to do with *amount* and not with *volume* – in other words, four buttons and four elephants are numerically equivalent. If we restrict children to working only with objects, how and when will we enable them to cope with this abstraction?

Further, if young children are intellectually limited and mathematical concepts are too abstract for them, these concepts must be broken down into simpler steps to correlate with the child's developmental stages. The argument is that children have much to learn before they are able to operate with numbers in the abstract. Counting is seen as dependent upon a child's grasp of the 'conservation' of number: the fact that the number of objects in a given set remains the same, however they are arranged. Conserving number, Piaget claimed, is beyond the reach of most children under seven, and prematurely imposing mathematical concepts on a child is ineffective. Consequently, educationalists have argued that there must therefore be other pre-counting tasks which are more appropriate to the *pre-operational* stage of development.[2] Enter sorting and matching. Prior to being able to label a collection of objects 'five', children must first grasp the fundamental idea of a 'set'; prior to being able to count a collection of objects successfully, they must engage in tasks that develop their sense of one-to-one correspondence.

The argument that all children must progress through some 'pre-number' tasks in order to be 'ready' for numeracy is now being questioned. That mathematics is intrinsically hard and must therefore be broken down into small steps for young children is still a pervasive view.[3] In this chapter, I will be arguing the case for supporting young children in more complex work.

Three additional points need to be made here. Firstly, by insisting that the child matures through predictable stages, Piaget under-emphasised the role of the teacher in the learning process. The teacher can have little influence upon a child's thinking where the child has to 'grow' mentally into the next stage.

Secondly, Piaget's emphasis on children as lone individuals, all necessarily working at their own pace, contributed to the prevalent view in 1970s mathematics education that it was appropriate to provide individualised (and usually published) learning programmes.

This hindered the role that interaction with peers played in the learning process, and further devalued the role of the teacher to a point where the teacher's main task was to monitor the child's progress (and even this was defined as progress through books or worksheets).

Finally, an over-dependence upon commercially produced materials has obstructed the development of children's ability to make decisions about what they do, how and when – in short, to think mathematically.

MOVING ON FROM PIAGET

Although Piaget's research was largely translated into the theory and practice of education, others in his era were putting forward views of the learning process that were radically different from those of Piaget.[4] Vygotsky (1962, 1978), Gattegno (1970, 1987) and Bruner (1960, 1986) all have the adult playing a crucial part in the development of the child. All stress the roles that interaction, communication and instruction play in the development of understanding. These and later critiques are now beginning to inform the ways that we operate with children in classrooms.

In common with Walkerdine (1982, 1984) and others (Gattegno, 1988; Vygotsky, 1978; Edwards and Mercer, 1987), I believe that mathematics is primarily an activity of the mind, closely bound up with the social context in which it takes place. It is interaction and discussion with people, rather than action on and with objects, that contributes to the development of abstract reasoning and mathematical thinking.

Within this chapter, I hope to put these issues into a classroom context by offering some alternative suggestions for practice, based on the recognition both that the role of the teacher is critical and that young children are powerful mathematical thinkers.

> ... none of [the psychologists'] advice was based on the observation and analysis of what goes on in classrooms. This has led to the under-emphasis in psychology of one of the most characteristic features of the educational process – its mutuality, that it is made up of the interactions between teachers and children.
>
> *Edwards, D. and Mercer, N. (1987), p.17*

I will start by outlining an alternative structure for an early years number syllabus, based on the belief that it is through working with numbers (rather than objects) that children become numerate.

THE 'TAUGHT NUMBER' SYLLABUS

Joanne, aged five, was asked to find out which of two small bags of plastic animals contained more animals, and to use a pencil and paper to help her. This is what happened. Her first bag contained ten dogs. She removed one dog, placed it at the top left-hand side of her paper and above it wrote '1'. She then removed another dog from the bag and placed it next to the first, writing '2'. She continued in a similar

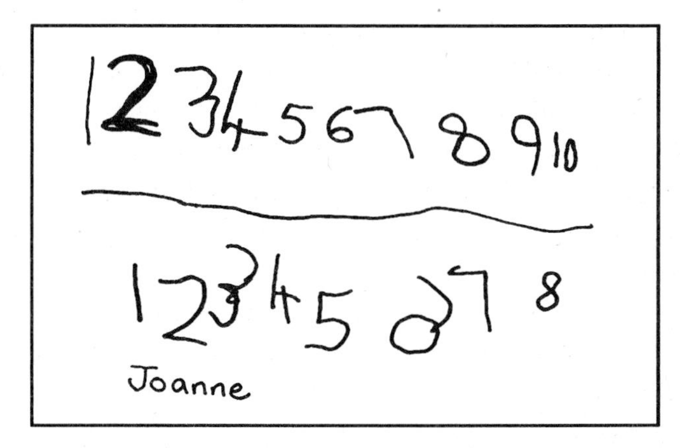

Figure 1

way, working across the top of her paper from left to right until all the dogs were in line and numbered. She occasionally asked me or a nearby child (also engaged in the activity) for help in writing a numeral. After completing the count of the dogs, she replaced them in the bag and went through the same process with a bag of eight cats. When she had finished she brought her paper to me (see Figure 1). She said:

> I have drawn a line so you can see that this is for the dogs and this is for the cats. There are more dogs because one more here and one more here is missing.

As she said 'here' each time, she touched the paper after the bottom figure 8.[5]

Let us examine the story of Joanne in relation to the test of Piaget's that has received the most scrutiny: that for the *conservation of number*. In this test, two rows of the same number of counters were arranged in one-to-one correspondence, and the child was asked whether there were the same number of counters in each row. If the child said 'yes', one row was then rearranged to make it appear longer, and the question was repeated. Piaget found that the majority of children under the age of seven maintained that the number of counters had changed as a result of the counters being rearranged. He therefore concluded that they could not conserve number.[6]

The notion of 'conservation' has been particularly influential in debates about children's numeracy. It is a notion that has significantly restricted our children's number curriculum, and through which we have seriously underestimated the capabilities and potential of young children. Children's ability to count has long been seen as dependent upon their grasp of one-to-one correspondence and their ability to 'conserve' an amount.[7] Thus the emphasis in early years number has been on developing these aspects. The argument is that children learn to conserve number by writing '3' next to various sets of three items arranged in different ways; and until this is established with each number in turn to ten, it is not appropriate to introduce any other numbers into the school curriculum. A child's ability to count will develop by practising pre-counting tasks such as drawing one flag on one sandcastle. Piaget is alive and well!

When working with Joanne, I had not deliberately set out to restructure Piaget's task; but there are some parallels. I had deliberately chosen two different amounts of objects for Joanne, amounts that I felt were on the edge of her ability to count: too few and the task would be facile, too many and she would be smothered. Piaget made the same amount take up different amounts of space. Joanne's two lines of numbers, with a different amount in each, appear very similar in the amount of space they take up; and yet her method left her in no doubt about which line contained more objects. She was not misled by the length of the lines. Why might this be?

Donaldson (1978) argues, and demonstrates, that young children are capable of abstract thinking which is embedded in an understandable context. This task made sense to Joanne: she was in control of it and how she tackled it. She was confident about making a numerical statement. In addition, I would argue that her method of recording helped her to see the difference between the amounts. It is very clear that '9' and '10' are missing in her second row.[8] I would argue further that the act of making the marks on paper helped her to do the mathematics.

The 'taught number' syllabus combines the processes of developing an understanding of certain concepts, acquiring particular facts and skills and building appropriate language and the confidence with which to discuss numbers. It is my contention that in order to learn how to count, and to understand what counting is, children must engage in counting and not something else. What is generally missing is the link between many children's well-developed sense of one-to-one correspondence and the vocalised counting sequence *one, two, three, four* – and beyond that, an understanding of the purpose of counting things.[9]

What alternatives are there to matching and conservation tasks for developing children's numeracy? We could consider children's early number experiences under three headings:

- counting – both ordinal and cardinal aspects;
- comparing amounts – both by direct comparison and by indirect comparison (counting);
- operations on and with numbers.

These headings are, of course, largely interdependent and will combine for many number tasks. The following discussion explores counting as a crucial area for developing young children's numeracy.

COUNTING

Here are three stories:

> (i) Lucy is sitting at the table with her mum and me. She wants to count us: 'One... two... three...' She stops: 'No, that's not right, I'm not three, I'm *four*.'

(ii) When I ask Ellen about her threading ('How many beads are there?'), she might successfully remember the counting words to eight and attach each word to one bead. I then ask 'How many did you say there were, Ellen?' She starts counting again: 'One, two, three...'

(iii) Jack might count all his thirty-two beads as follows: '...twenty-seven, twenty-eight, twenty-nine, twenty-ten, twenty-eleven, twenty-twelve. I've got twenty-twelve here.'

What do these children know and understand about counting?

Counting is a complex activity. Young children have many things to learn and remember when they are learning to count. They have to recall each number word in the correct order; to co-ordinate hand, eye and voice; and somehow to keep track of what has been counted and what has not. To understand counting, children need to realise that (irrespective of the order in which objects are counted and how they are arranged) the last number we say is the important word, telling us how many there are in the set. I can observe children at different points in connecting all these skills and understandings.

Add to this the fact that a number word can be used in different senses:

✧ a label, as in 'I am four' [years old];
✧ a position in a sequence, as in *one, two, three, four*;
✧ a description of a set of objects, as in 'there are four here';
✧ what I say when I touch this (fourth) object when counting this set. Notably, I am touching one object, but I am saying 'four'.

Ordinal counting – learning the words and the order – has been a much-undervalued activity in early years mathematics. The emphasis has been on activities to develop young children's cardinal number sense: knowledge of the amount in a set. The argument is that children should not meet a number ordinally until they understand it cardinally. However, a child's cardinal and ordinal knowledge of numbers do not develop separately, since they are clearly connected. Working on both together will enrich a child's number knowledge.

Young children can and should engage with the number system – ordinal counting above 20 – from an early age, while also engaging in tasks that help to develop their grasp of the 'size' of a number. There are many partial 'understandings' about numbers which children have to grasp.[10] Learning that there is a word for a number and where it 'belongs' in the sequence is one of these; so is developing an idea of the 'size' of numbers. As with words in everyday language, their hearing and using number words is exactly what helps children's understanding of them to mature.

It is notable that we concentrate on what is arguably the most difficult section of the counting sequence, i.e. the numbers below 20, with the youngest children. From working only on these numbers, children could form the impression that there is no pattern to our counting sequence, but only an accumulating number of new words to memorise. Exploring the structure of our number system with young children involves hearing, saying and seeing the numbers in position; getting to know the counting sequence by reciting the number names, forwards and backwards; and developing children's fluency with the sequence by not always starting at 1 and stopping at 10. For example: 'Let's start at 22 and count. Listen... and when you can hear the pattern, join in. 22, 23, 24, ...'. Discussion will reveal what the children have noticed, such as the fact that the numbers all begin with 'twenty-' or that they follow a '2, 3, 4 ...' pattern.

Ordinal counting games such as these have to be a regular activity to be worthwhile. Placing vocal stress on the unit digits can help to 'crack the code', enabling children to predict the counting sequence with only one new word to learn for each ten units. Helping children to see numbers in position involves giving them access to number lines (to 100) and to a variety of number squares, as well as to calculators,[11] and encouraging them to share what they notice with others.

Linking the counting sequence to the counting of objects involves co-ordinating the voice with the finger. Work on one-to-one correspondence involves reminding the child to say the number when touching or pointing to the object. Children need to practise counting with objects that are moveable, to allow them to organise the count. The task of counting printed images is very different.

The act of counting engages all of a young child's energies, and it is difficult for the child to pay attention to the purpose of counting (that is, to establish 'how many' there are). In an interesting article, Van Den Brink (1984) demonstrates that pausing during a count and drawing a child's attention to the last number spoken, helps the child to make the step between counting and giving a number label to the whole set[12]. For example, stopping with your finger in position during a count of objects and asking: 'How many is that so far..?' 'Oh, yes, 5, right, ... 5, 6, 7...'

In addition, asking children to observe and comment on someone else's counting helps them to concentrate on the process, showing what they know, without the act of counting getting in the way. Children can be asked to spot 'mistakes' in counts, for example, 'Teddy is going to count these crayons. Watch her to make sure she gets it right.' Teddy can legitimately make some common counting mistakes, such as counting an object more than once, missing out a number or getting paw and eye out of synchronisation.

COMPARING

Counting is a form of measure, allowing amounts to be compared indirectly. This is the purpose of counting. Presenting children with pictures of two groups of objects and asking them to 'draw lines to match the eggs with the eggcups' does not involve them in any mathematical thinking about amounts. The question 'Which has most?' is a counting – not a matching – question. Comparing amounts, as in the task offered to Joanne, provides a clear purpose for counting. Munn's research (1994) suggests that activities involving counting with adults for a clear purpose would help to establish an understanding of the reason why we count (just as children understand that the purpose of reading is to access meaning).

This has clear links to the work of Donaldson (1978). She argues that the main stumbling block children face when they start school is the emphasis on the acquisition of skills isolated from any context, at a time when the sense they make of experience relies heavily on contextual clues. It is possible to ask young children counting questions that make 'human sense', in the words of Donaldson, and are accessible to them. Questions that involve them working with something as complex as numbers and yet allow them the opportunity to organise the task themselves. Questions such as 'Let's each take a handful of these cubes. Whose hand do you think holds the most?' or inviting children to take a handful of cubes from a tray containing cubes of two colours and asking them 'Which colour did you pick more of?' The next step might be to make a record of the handful to see whether I pull out more red cubes tomorrow: an indirect comparison across time. Over time, varying the type of object and mixing large and small items will help the children to focus on amount rather than size.

OPERATIONS

It is curious that despite Piaget's emphasis on the importance of practical work in helping children understand number, as well as of not presenting children with a mathematical concept until they are developmentally 'ready', much early years experience in relation to learning about the processes of addition and subtraction has still been through formal arithmetic divorced from apparatus. But learning how to change numbers by operating on them is not a matter of learning about manipulating symbols. Repeated practice of 'sums' does not help a child understand how to add up. The formal notation of '3 + 2 =' is just that, a widely accepted means of writing an addition problem on paper. It does not contribute to an understanding of number.

Children as young as two can comprehend the idea of 'one more', and the idea that one more and one more and one more... leads to lots; and also, the idea of continually taking one away until they are 'all gone'. Understanding number operations begins with the realisation that we can change amounts to make them larger or smaller, or to make them disappear altogether.

Many of the early school activities involving children in operating with numbers use the idea of combining sets. For example: 'If I have three in this hand and two in this hand, how many do I have altogether?' When we combine numbers, a new total is reached. An equally important idea is that of partitioning, where a total quantity is given – for example, 'I have a total of five beads. Some are in this hand and some are in this hand. How many could be in each hand?' Working with a fixed quantity and 'partitioning' it makes it easier to move from object to mind and back again. For example: 'I am thinking of four beads. Can you imagine four beads? Now hide one, how many can I see?'

Children will only feel confident at this mental activity when they have actually played similar hiding games. Martin Hughes' (1986) work with very young children used a box from which he removed and replaced bricks, asking questions such as 'How many are there now?' I have used this idea successfully to deepen children's knowledge of number bonds by focusing on one fixed quantity at a time. The advantage of this is that the children are (even at five years old) very aware of what we are working on. I can even be explicit: 'All our hiding games are going to be about six this week'.[13]

A note about numerical equality. There seems to be an intrinsic human desire for balance and symmetry. Observe children playing with bricks. Number activities need to include 'making the same amount as mine' and then changing it. Young children tend to make two groups match in amount by adding more items to the group with fewer. What seems more difficult for them, is to remove some from the larger group to balance the sets. Perhaps because outside school, 'more' is a more commonly discussed experience than 'less', children seem to have a firmer grasp of 'more' as a concept than of 'less' or 'fewer'. Is this why many seem to find addition easier than subtraction?

Children's satisfaction with, and interest in, equal groupings and 'balance' can be useful in developing their mental arithmetic. A young child may be able to volunteer that 10 and 10 make 20, or that 100 and 100 make 200; and yet the same child might find it difficult to add 5 and 6. Just as we can build children's knowledge of ordinal number around the strings they already know, we need to build their learning of new number facts around those they already know.

SYMBOLS AND MARK-MAKING

There appears to be a contradiction between research demonstrating that young children arrive at school with substantial knowledge about number and research pinpointing the difficulties children have with school mathematics (Hughes, 1981; Walkerdine, 1981,1988; Kennard, 1985, Behr et al, 1980). The work of Hughes examined this apparent paradox. He pinpointed the difficulty children have in linking their concrete understandings with the formal symbols of written arithmetic. More written recording takes place in number work than in any other area of mathematics. Commonly, such recording is exactly prescribed. This is despite accumulated evidence from the last century showing unequivocally that too early an introduction to formal arithmetic hinders children's numeracy.[14]

There is a strong human tendency to symbolise our thinking. From cave paintings onwards, people have used marks to convey a message. For very young children one of the exciting discoveries with picture books is that the print – the verbal message – remains unchanged whoever reads the book. Unlike writing, a drawing cannot be 'read' in the same way each time and by everyone.

A symbol or sign stands for something. Mathematical signs are conventions, and a standard notation is an agreed set of signs: a formalised code or language which initiates can, in theory, read without any confusion or ambiguity.[15] However, many of us have memories of finding this language extremely difficult to understand. How can we remove some of the mystery of conventional mathematical notation?

APPARATUS

Piaget viewed activity with objects as the essential starting-point for developing numeracy. However, stress on manipulating objects is not the whole answer. Young children learning to decode '3 + 4 = ' are usually taught a physical algorithm involving the moving and regrouping of bricks or counters. The physical movement of the bricks is intended to help interpret the written statement. In fact, what is written and what is done in the head bear little relation to what the child is doing with the bricks.[16] A ten-year-old was attempting a number of subtractions similar to this one, with base ten materials:

$$\begin{array}{r} 153 \\ 27\,- \\ \hline \\ \hline \end{array}$$

With mutterings and pencil sucking, she completed the answers quite quickly and correctly. She then turned to the base ten apparatus on her table and moved it about. In her book, she crossed out the '5' to write '4' and inserted a '1' next to the '3'. When I asked what she was doing, she said: 'I can do them, but Mr Williams doesn't like us to do it without the blocks.'

This child has a method for correctly subtracting a two-digit number from a three-digit number. Both the apparatus and the required pencil marks appear to be superfluous. But she is obedient and does what she is expected to do.

I am certainly not arguing here for less use of apparatus in the teaching of number. I am arguing for more careful consideration of the role that both apparatus and mark-making play in learning. What sort of mark-making is involved here?

WHAT'S INSIDE?

Hughes (1982) describes a fascinating task he gave some very young children. The children were given four identical containers, each containing a different small amount of bricks. The children were asked to represent each amount by making a mark on a paper lid for each container. I have tried this activity with different children on many occasions.[17]

The symbols shown in Figure 2 belong to Emma, Ceri and Emily, who were just turning five. I provided identical yoghurt pots, paper and pens and asked the question: 'Can you put something on the paper lid to help you remember what is inside the pot?' The top left mark is for the empty container; this was drawn first. Ceri said, 'Oh, it's got none in, I don't know how to put none... Oh yes, I do.' Following this, Emma immediately put a '0' on all the other lids. Meanwhile, Emily quietly wrote '3' (bottom right). Ceri then told Emma to 'Put a 1'. Ceri corrected her resulting squiggle to a '1' (top right); this was the lid for the one-pot. This left the bottom left lid, which was the pot containing two: two circles (tallies), one for each brick, were drawn by Emma. Afterwards, this was the only pot she could identify; she identified this pot correctly over the period of the following two weeks.

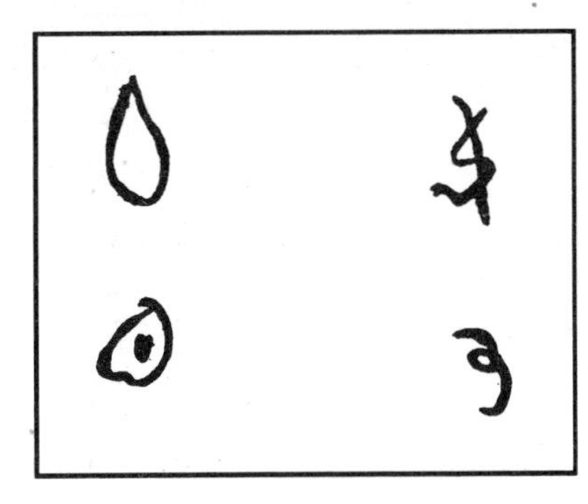

Figure 2

PROTO-NUMBERS

The work of Hughes is directly replicable in a classroom, demonstrating that young children are able to use and decode symbols where the activity of symbol-making is meaningful for them. Over a period of time, with many different children, I have found that both the variety of response and the threads of similarity across responses matched very closely those documented by Hughes. Hughes describes children as young as three years old making decisions about how to symbolise something. Referring to the historical development of our present numerical system, Rotman (1985) points to the historical precedence of signs such as notches and tally marks as '...a record left by a counting subject, particular representations of numbers in a written medium.' (p.24). He calls these signs 'proto-numbers'. The development of tasks asking children to invent a mark – a 'proto-number' – could be a way forward in helping children to connect their pre-school, informal numerical understanding with formal mathematical mark-making.

When a class of reception children is asked to paint *When we all went to the fire station*, twenty-five similar paintings are not expected. Also, it may not be surprising to receive one that is a 'scribble'. In relation to writing, Graves (1983) believes that children can write from the first day of school – 'Writing, of course, must be liberally interpreted.' (p.18). For Graves, children learn to write only by writing, not by doing something else entirely. The crucial point is that the teacher responds to and builds upon what the child offers, thus giving children confidence in their own voices. Writing conventions and skills are introduced alongside tasks stimulating the young child as a generator of writing. This attempt to build literacy around what children already know and can do has been further articulated through the 'developmental' writing approach. Could this be extended to mathematics – and more particularly to number?[18]

MATHEMATICAL MESSAGES

Is it possible to introduce mathematical mark-making that could make 'human sense' to a young child? There are several strands to this. The first strand is actively encouraging children to solve problems like 'Can you find a way of pricing these packages?', 'Use the pencil to show how many are inside here.' In other words, to seek out situations where a mark is a solution to a problem.

Another strand is building on what children already know from outside school about numbers and numerical messages. Children's 'home learning' becomes obvious through their role play. Role play is also rich in opportunities to build children's confidence in leaving mathematical marks. 'The Post Office' offers a range of suitable tasks: messages to write on the pad by the telephone, scales and parcels to weigh and label, stamps to purchase, price lists to devise, a calculator and pad for calculations, bills and receipts to write.... Actively seeking out opportunities to engage in mathematical recording, as messages for themselves and for others, might help children to bridge the gap between a practical activity, mathematical thinking and symbolic recording.

Tasks which require children to generate signs and symbols should also lead them to compare and discuss various signs and symbols and their effectiveness. More formalised and conventional signs and symbols can be introduced alongside the informal, with discussion about which are appropriate for various situations.

A third strand is always providing writing apparatus alongside physical apparatus or a practical mathematical task. There is an expectation here that some mathematics will end up on the paper. Inviting children to 'Find a way of showing that on paper', or to 'Put something on the paper to show your friend what you have done', emphasises the purpose of written mathematics and reinforces the idea that marks can convey meaning. Most tasks with apparatus are ephemeral and result in no long-term record of the activity; note-taking would help to 'place' the activity and the moment – 'Oh, I remember this, we made a long, long snake with the Plasticine!' If we promote such mathematical note-taking, then the symbol, the activity and the thinking are woven together. It encourages children to think using both apparatus *and* symbols, moving between the two as necessary.

Most mathematical marks made by children in school are not related to anything happening. Numbers are written in boxes, lines are drawn between sets. However, the teacher might say: 'Keep some notes as you work with this', or ask 'Can you put something on paper so you know where to start tomorrow?' Such notes made by children can be used to focus later discussion about what they have been doing and thinking. Like Graves, I believe the term 'mathematical notes' needs to be interpreted liberally. An environment can be fostered where children refer to their notes in order to develop their work further, to report back on their thinking, or to pick up where they have left off. A piece of child-initiated mathematical writing might be used to begin a mathematical session or to generate further mathematical activity:

> Can you remember what we did with the Cuisenaire rods on Tuesday? Look at your note book.... Look at what Joanne did yesterday. What can you tell from what she has written here? Now let's try....[19]

Recording in mathematics has an additional role. We should recognise the role that mark-making might play in organising one's thoughts. Think again about Joanne's method of writing the numbers of dogs and cats (see page 23). The pencil and paper helped her to think, slowing her down, somehow 'placing' her thinking. Most mathematical recording with young children takes place when the activity is over, or instead of a practical activity. In Joanne's task, the recording (mark-making) was integral to the activity. Perhaps we should try suggesting 'Here are a pencil and paper' when a child is having difficulties with bricks.

THE TEACHER'S ROLE AND CHILDREN'S VOICES

In *Children's Minds* (1978), Margaret Donaldson challenges much of the intellectual framework on which our teaching is based. She argues that teachers have both underestimated the rational powers of young children and ignored the importance of context in interpreting the meaning of what children say. This is a damning statement. What does it mean exactly?

How I present a mathematical task fundamentally affects how successful the children are at this task. I must be aware of the possibility of deliberately 'catching them out' by closing down their responses.[20] My task as a teacher is to present mathematics which gives children opportunities to show me how they understand the problem. This requires that I listen and ask the sort of questions that allows for a range of answers, without pushing the child into a prescribed response. Let us consider how this might be attempted when working with young children on large numbers.

LARGE NUMBERS

In my view, large numbers enrich the mathematical experience of young children. Not all children under seven live in houses with numbers less than 10. We catch buses, we spend money, we travel. Children can and do talk about large numbers and do show some understanding of them. Indeed, what understanding do *we* have of a number such as 45 678 923, or 0.00004? I might start by providing a calculator, pencil and paper and asking 'Show me what you can do today.What numbers can you make appear? Let's compare your numbers with Emma's numbers.' Calculators are a very powerful means of focusing a young child's outside-school number experiences and examining some numbers in the abstract, as numbers. This helps to make some links between 'embedded' and 'disembedded' modes of thinking (in Donaldson's argument).

Calculators should have caused a revolution in our teaching of number, since they allow very young children to display extraordinary powers of computation.[21] In my experience, they have not caused such a revolution. We might ask ourselves why. The problem with providing calculators is that we cannot be sure how they will be used. The calculator immediately gives young children access to big numbers, and we cannot control the mathematics. This makes my role as a teacher difficult. How should we respond if the child keys in a number too large for her or him to read? One answer to this question is to say something positive, to use the situation to our advantage:

> That's a large number, I'll read it to you... What big numbers do you know?... Can you make a larger number?...

Looking at the piece of children's work in Figure 3, what should we choose to respond to: the 'mistakes' or the abilities? David Tripp's comment seems pertinent here:

> Students do misunderstand, but it is seldom because they cannot understand: most often it is because they understand something else.
>
> Tripp, D. (1993)

Figure 3

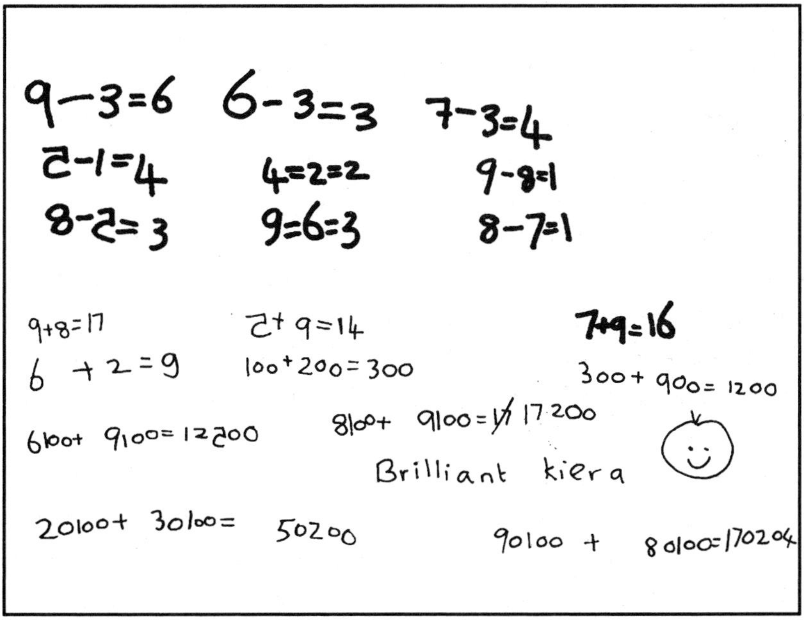

9−3=6 6-3=3 7-3=4
5-1=4 4=2=2 9-8=1
8-5=3 9=6=3 8-7=1

9+8=17 5+9=14 7+9=16
6 + 2 = 9 100+200=300 300+ 900= 1200
6100+ 9100= 12500 8100+ 9100 = 1~~7~~ 17200
Brilliant kiera
20100+ 30100= 50200 90100 + 80100=170204

CHALLENGING QUESTIONS

Children need opportunities to express themselves, to struggle with describing what they think and what they 'see'. We need to hear them speak. 'What do you see in your mind when I say three?' is a legitimate question to ask a young child. 'Close your eyes and think of three fingers. Show me. Close your eyes and think of three fingers a different way.... Tell me....' Mathematics is within the mind. Mental imagery is achieved by people working inside themselves to create meaning, and is thus an integral part of mathematics at all levels (Gattegno, 1983; Bruner, 1975, Dawson, 1982; Plunkett, 1979, 1983). It is a crucial part of becoming numerate. Mental 'games' can be played to build children's confidence in working in their heads with numbers. Allowing children to glimpse a small number of buttons on a tray and asking them to describe what they have seen may be difficult at first and more than one glimpse may be necessary. But young children deserve to be asked challenging questions. 'Close your eyes and imagine five buttons. Tell me how they are. Now move them about. Stop. Tell me what you see now.'

A *challenging* question for a four-year-old is one that requires her or him to take the initiative in answering it. What is challenging for us is hearing what we don't expect.

Asking challenging questions means that sometimes we do not get answers. This does not mean that we stop asking the question, as eventually someone (if not us) will provide an answer. Children need to get used to being asked questions. Asking a four-year-old 'How did you work that out?', the reply is often of the kind: 'I just did it'. Perhaps a detailed answer is not necessary: it is enough that we draw their attention to the process of them doing something in their heads, helping them to realise that only they can access and control their thought processes.

> Unless time for reflection is provided, learning from experience does not take place.
>
> John Mason (1982), p.22

> Activity by itself is not enough. It is the sense that is made of it that matters.
>
> Driver, R. (1983), p.49; in Edwards and Mercer (1987), p.126

Neither children nor adults learn directly from experience. They need the opportunity to reflect on that experience, to make sense of it in relation to other experiences. Doing this enables them to move from a particular situation to a general one. Children need to be made aware of their own reflection in order to be able to recall and repeat the process. How might I do this? To start with, I might simply say 'Did you notice that you worked that out without using your fingers?' or 'Did you find that easy or hard?' On occasions I might ask, 'Tell me something that you have learned today'. Thomas is five years old and has just completed a task making paper cylinders of different sizes:

> Helen: I want you all to think a minute about something you have found out this morning. Just sit and think by yourself.
> (Pause)
> Now put up your hand if you have found out something you want to tell us all.
> Thomas: I have found out something. I have found out about big.
> Helen: About big?
> Thomas: Yes, you see, I thought this was big, and then I made this one, and then this was big. And then I made this one, and it was big. And then I might make another one and that might be big, and then another one might be big... so I thought, what is big? Yes, what is big?

Thomas is unusual in that he has responded very clearly to a reflective question. He has lifted himself out of the particular events of the morning and made a general statement. More usually, we might receive a description of the particular events. But it is only by asking such a question that there is the possibility of such a response.

Reflective questions need careful timing: we often cannot reflect on what we have done immediately. If we rush too quickly from task to task, thinking we have to teach something new each time, we are not allowing children time to make sense of their experiences. There is pressure to 'get through the curriculum', but we need to be confident enough to resist this by asking ourselves what the curriculum is. We need to ask ourselves powerful questions such as:

> Why am I doing this with these children? What is the purpose of this task? Am I doing this merely because it is in the scheme of work? Am I convinced about what I am doing? Indeed, am I teaching the mathematics or just teaching 'the page'?

CONCLUSION

From the early 1960s, writers on mathematics education began to put forward a style of teaching and learning strongly based on practical work and on 'readiness' to learn. The argument was that with the provision of an appropriate environment, children would gradually develop the sequential concepts on which later learning is based. In this model, the teacher's role is to monitor each individual child's progress in order to provide suitable and carefully defined concrete experiences.

Piaget's theory describes the young child as having strictly limited cognitive abilities. The work of Hughes and Donaldson, among others, questions this view. Both argue that in situations that make 'human sense' to her or him, the child can and will operate successfully.

In addition, Piaget's arguments imply that, met at the optimum time, learning abstract mathematics should not present a problem. Donaldson's work indicates that we all have problems with what she calls 'disembedded' thinking: thinking beyond the bounds of 'human sense'. This suggests that mathematics could present a problem to children whenever it is taught, if we fail to tackle issues of context.

Thus, in whatever we provide, we must work on connecting 'embedded' thinking to abstract thinking. We are doing young children no favours by confining their numerical experiences to working only with objects, or indeed only with traditional mathematical symbols.

The approach we take to written mathematics holds one key to helping children start to work in the abstract. There is a fundamental misunderstanding of the role that recording and mark-making can play for young children learning mathematics. Until we encourage children to use their own written marks to help them think, there will be gaps between object, thought and symbol.

While I would not want to argue with one significant legacy of Piaget, the assertion that children need to understand what they are learning, I am aware of the shortfalls of our present number curriculum for the under-sevens. Sorting and matching tasks were accepted as the first, concrete steps towards learning about abstract number; yet an eighteen-month-old child can sort in quite sophisticated ways. Witness the child who selects only the circular shapes to post into a posting toy,[22] or all the red LEGO bricks to make a tower. Children are also able to 'match' one-to-one long before they start school – for example, most two-year-olds realise the 'mistake' of putting two socks on one foot. What can I, as reception class teacher, ask children to do at sixty months that extends and deepens these understandings? A rich numerical environment is one where children's previous numerical experiences are acknowledged and taken advantage of, while they learn how to use imagery, equipment and language to describe and reflect upon particular things in order to make sense of them in relation to the general.

The contention of this chapter has been that children's numeracy is fundamentally affected by what the teacher provides and how the teacher behaves. We cannot underestimate how much our interaction with children, and their interaction with each other, affects their success and ability in number. The teaching of number involves working with numbers in all their complexity:

> When facing complexity, one is forced to do one's own breaking down; but having done it, one is aware of how the pieces fit together into a dynamic whole; and a constant awareness of the whole makes it easier to understand the pieces.[23]
>
> Saunders, K. (1977)

This chapter is based on a talk given to the Association of Teachers of Mathematics to open their Easter conference, 1996. The text of this talk appears in the journal Mathematics Teaching *(A.T.M.), September 1996, Vol. 156.*

NOTES

1. Piaget's influence on education has been substantial, despite the fact that he was a research biologist who did not intentionally seek to influence educational practice. Piaget formed his theory of cognitive development from a series of laboratory-based tasks performed on single children of various ages.
2. From eighteen months to seven years, children are (in theory) at the pre-operational stage, where their thinking is dominated by what they see. From the ages of around seven to eleven, children are at the concrete operational stage and are incapable of higher-order skills such as logical deduction or abstract reasoning.
3. The 'small steps' argument is applied both to young children and to children experiencing difficulties with number.
4. It is probably relevant that the translation of Piaget's findings into English took place at a time when dissatisfaction with 'traditional' education methods, based on rote learning and memorisation of facts, was growing. It is easy to see how attractive Piaget's theory was to many 'progressives' who found in Piaget a rationale for more 'child-centred' education. Notable in this respect were Nathan Issacs (1960, 1961) and J.H. Flavell (1963).
5. Williams, H. (1989)
6. A description of this and others of Piaget's tests relevant to the teaching of number is given in Hughes (1986).
7. Piaget presented a child with a line of six buttons, first spread out and then bunched together, and asked 'How many are there now?' The child would say that the amount had changed and recount the collection. The work of Donaldson and Hughes offers an alternative story.
8. Identifying an item as 'missing' is very familiar to young children.
9. Cf. Penelope Munn's research with nursery children (1994).
10. A two-year-old is capable of saying some number-words in some order – one, two, three, four; but they are not often reliably able to count out four things.
11. Generating a count by using the 'constant function' facility helps to connect words with a visible number.
12. Van Den Brink's article contains other interesting and innovative ideas for teaching children about counting.
13. Baratta-Lorton's innovative book (1976) describes three games of this kind which practice the same idea in slightly different contexts.

14. See McIntosh (1979) for a résumé.

15. Liebeck (1985) views mathematical statements as unambiguous. I am not so sure that they are. Consider the range of contexts that could be conveyed by the expression '$20 \times 4 =$ '. The sign $\times$ is a condensed form of many particular situations.

16. Hughes (1986) and Jones worked with children up to the age of eight years to see whether they would use conventional '+' and '–' signs to represent an addition or subtraction problem demonstrated with bricks. He found that not one child in his study did so, although they had all been using these signs almost daily in their arithmetic.

17. Williams, H (1989).

18. The authors of *Mathematics with Reason* (Atkinson, S. (ed) 1992) draw parallels between the approaches embedded by development writing and by mathematics teaching and learning.

19. Marion Bird's exciting book (1991) uses case studies to describe young children engaging in mathematical explorations involving recording.

20. We can illustrate 'catching out' by reference to Piaget's conservation task. By drawing the child's attention to the rearrangement of the counters, it could be argued that we are encouraging children to agree that something has changed.

21. As demonstrated by those teachers and children involved in the CAN project, part of the PrIME project based at Homerton College, Cambridge, during the late 1980s. See Chapter 3.

22. Perhaps thinking, though not able to verbalise, 'The ones I can do.'

23. This statement is based on the traditional concept of the 'hermeneutic circle' of understanding.

CHAPTER 3

READING MATHEMATICS

A NEW APPROACH TO TEACHING AND LEARNING MATHS

Primary maths has taken a hammering in recent years. The evidence of both research and practice has not been comforting for teachers or pupils. The report produced by the London Mathematical Society (1995) suggests that, even where secondary pupils do achieve a moderate interim success in maths, they are less than competent when it comes to the mathematical skills required for further work and study in related subjects (such as physics and engineering). Further down the age scale, the evidence collected by Helvia Bierhoff (1996) in the report entitled *The Foundations of Numeracy* – and to some extent confirmed by the OFSTED reports (1996) – suggests that too many English children aged seven to ten are neither sufficiently confident nor adequately competent with simple arithmetic operations. To add to the generally depressed mood, we have witnessed the publication of several other pieces of research, including the international comparisons published in the Gatsby Seminars (1995) carried out by the Professor David Burghes and his team at Exeter, which strongly suggest cause for concern. In summary, we are forced to the conclusion that our pupils at all stages of the schooling process are performing less successfully than those in other, comparable societies; less adequately than their equivalent cohorts of twenty-plus years ago; and less competently than is thought to be necessary or desirable for their own needs, both academic and pragmatic.

In the face of this gloomy diagnosis, many teachers have adopted a defensive posture. And indeed, from the teacher's perspective, the criticisms appear unfair given the number of curriculum changes and pedagogical initiatives which have been imposed on teachers over the last fifteen years. It feels as if, over this period, teachers have been subjected to a succession of changes in approach and new theories about how children learn mathematics. Having struggled to come to terms with the implications for classroom practice and teaching approaches, teachers may reasonably complain that they are being blamed for the consequences of these changes – even when these consequences were predicted by some of the teachers required to implement the changes.

However, it is worth looking at both the genesis and the implications of some of these 'radical ideas' in mathematics education over the last 15 years. And any such endeavour must start with the publication of the Cockcroft Report (1982).

THE COCKCROFT REPORT

The publication of this extremely influential report invited a 'sea-change' in the approach to teaching primary maths. This transformation can be summarised as follows:

1. Maths was no longer conceived as a body of knowledge to be transferred from one person to another. Rather, the Cockcroft Report (both implicitly and explicitly) drew upon a notion of maths as a kind of language, a structured system of signification and communication. Thus, we moved from thinking of maths as a sort of 'bag of facts and figures, procedures and concepts' to recognising maths as a means of communicating.

2. The emphasis shifted from *facts to be learned* to *problems to be solved*. A matching focus on problem-solving strategies was developed; in extreme cases, this led to the production of a taxonomy of such strategies in a 'how-to-solve-problems' kit. Thus many resource materials and published schemes began to emerge in a sector called 'problem solving'; and the GCSE maths course came to include a more practical aspect whereby pupils would investigate a particular mathematical or 'real-life' problem and find ways of solving it. The move from facts and procedures to problem solving led to a perception on the part of some teachers and many parents that 'getting the answer right' was no longer what mattered in mathematics: the child had to demonstrate an ability to 'investigate the problem'.

3. In parallel with this stress on the problem-solving aspects of mathematics, we witnessed an insistence on *discovery learning*, as opposed to the notion of learning as imbibing knowledge. Thus teaching became construed as facilitating children's discoveries, rather than as transmitting knowledge. Children could be lead to 'discover' mathematical facts and procedures, rather than being presented with formal strategies and techniques.

4. There was an emphasis on *activity* rather than written and technical proficiency. Thus pupils were encouraged to explore by cutting out, creating and playing with mathematical shapes and figures. To a certain extent, this replaced the conventional repetition of written exercises. Indeed, without anyone specifying exactly why, the whole idea of written practice began to have a bad name: it was regarded as, to some extent, a sign of inferior practice in teaching.

5. It became a matter of crucial importance to provide a physical representation of mathematical operations and procedures. The justifications for this demand were always quasi-Piagetian in tone, though the extreme lengths to which the idea is sometimes taken owes little or nothing to Piaget's actual writings. Thus all written operations and symbolic representations were explained in terms of a physical realisation. One result of the insistence upon the importance of a concrete physical representation has been an associated reduction in the amount of attention paid to mental, syntactic and semantic formulations. We can see how this has affected mathematics teaching if we look at some examples (see Figure 1).

In these examples, we can see that the emphasis on physical representations of mathematical concepts and operations may be counterproductive. In the first example, the insistence on addition as the combining of two sets encourages children to count both sets – a practice we need them to abandon as fast as they can. (If this is doubted, think how slow it is to perform 27 + 3 in this way!) What we need is for children to recognise the 'counting on' aspect of addition as soon as possible. Thus we require a focus upon the ordinal

Operation	Physical representation	Mental/Semantic/ Syntactic
8 + 4 = eight and four is...	count eight bricks, count four bricks, then count total	look at 8 on number line count on 4 8 and what makes 12?
12 ÷ 3 = twelve divide by three is...	count out twelve bricks share into three piles how many in each pile?	how many 3s in 12? what times 3 is 12?
read 108	use base ten equipment to set out one hundred, no tens and eight ones	count from 99 99, 100, 101, 102... use number line
read 1.9	using base ten equipment or colour 10 x 10 grids, represent aspect of a decimal as 1 part in ten, parts in ten, etc.	use position on a number line count: 1, 1.1, 1.2, 1.3, 1.4, 1.5

Figure 1

aspect of numbers (as in the number line) and the development of *mental* rather than physical counting strategies.

Similarly, in the second example, the characterisation of division as 'sharing' – so beloved of this era – is unhelpful as the children progress in their mathematics. Given that they will need to abandon this metaphor and come to see division as the inverse of multiplication, it is debatable whether or not the 'sharing' model helps in the long run. It is impractical to do 56 ÷ 8 as a 'sharing': it has to be seen as the inverse of multiplication – something times 8 is 56. Construing division as a 'sharing' operation takes no account of where we are trying to take the children, mathematically speaking.

In the third and fourth examples, we have a tension between the physical modelling of the number using base ten equipment and the mental dimension developed using the number line. Seeing the numbers as positions in a line or series is a much more productive means of ordering for the purpose of seeing which numbers are more or less than or come 'in between' other numbers. 'Which numbers come in between 1.2 and 2.1?' is a much easier question to answer using a number line than using in Dienes blocks.

The Cockcroft Report and the ideas it represented resulted in a change not only in our approach to the teaching of mathematics, but also in the ways in which we thought about the subject and spoke about how children learn it. Post-Cockcroft, and throughout the late 1980s, teachers were being encouraged and even exhorted to transform their mathematical pedagogy. What came to be construed as 'good mathematics teaching' embodied many of the above-mentioned factors. Teachers were required to demonstrate an investigational or problem-solving approach to the teaching and learning of mathematics. The children should 'discover' rather than be told, and ideally should come to invent their own strategies or procedures rather than be instructed in their use. Mathematical explanations, particularly those supplied to children aged five to eleven years, were expected to involve the physical or concrete realisations of the operation or concept. Increasingly, here and in North America, children were construed as active learners rather than the passive recipients of knowledge assumed by earlier and more traditional pedagogies.

COCKCROFT – NOT FAR ENOUGH!

The problem with the Cockcroft Report is that it goes both too far and not far enough. Although it attempted to move away from a view of maths as a body of knowledge (a content-oriented approach), in practice it reinforced precisely this configuration. The accent on problem solving meant that mathematics became conceived as a vast array of 'mathematical problems', ready and waiting to be solved. These problems, along with their possible and traditional solutions, constituted precisely that 'body of knowledge' which we were attempting to jettison. Thus the construction of maths as a language – a structured and structuring system of signification, relations and communication – became submerged in the more traditional and prevailing conception of maths as a 'bag of content', a huge conglomeration of related facts, patterns and problems. It is in this sense that we may complain that the Cockcroft Report did not go far enough. Although it certainly paved the way for linguistic or syntactic constructions of mathematics, in practice it reverted to the view that maths is a body of knowledge. The only difference with tradition lay in the construction of this body of knowledge as a series of problems and possible solutions, rather than as a set of facts, operations and given procedures.

THE COCKCROFT REPORT – GOING TOO FAR

In other respects, the Cockcroft Report moved pedagogical practice too far in a particular direction. In my view, this shift may be said to have been at least partly responsible for the decline in the standard of pupils' mathematical performance. We have mentioned three distinct elements which combine to produce the 'post-Cockcroft' approach. The first is discovery learning, the second is the activity-led curriculum, and the third is the insistence that mathematical understanding is achieved or enhanced solely through the concrete physical representation of mathematical concepts or operations. These three facets are, of course, connected by a Piagetian thread. Piaget (1926) argued that cognitive development is prior to learning, and that understanding proceeds via the physical enactment of concrete operations. These ideas have become a part of the general ideology of early childhood education and, to a large extent, have underpinned the arguments and debates in primary education. Cockcroft reinforced much of this, by then dominant, ideology. Three implications of this general approach are worth considering in detail:

1. READINESS

Children must be *ready* to learn certain concepts. Cognitive development, it is argued, is prior to learning, and proceeds in stages. Children move on from one developmental stage to the next. Therefore it is necessary for a child to have reached the appropriate developmental stage before a particular topic or subject is taught. If concepts or mathematical entities (such as 'large' numbers) are presented too early, before the child is 'ready', this may be actively harmful. Thus the notions of 'reading readiness' and 'numerical readiness' become guiding principles for us as teachers; and also, in the event of a child not learning something, the argument that he or she was not ready will obviate the need for any close scrutiny of the actual teaching involved.

2. UNDERSTANDING

There is now a general insistence that children must *understand* what they are doing at all stages in mathematics. This is so much taken for granted that it seems almost wicked to question it. However, it is a very recent idea in the practice of formal education. Fifty years ago, it would have been assumed that children should be taught to perform all manner of mathematical rituals and procedures without any concern at all about whether they understood them. It would also have been assumed that if they practised these things to the point of automatic performance, sooner or later the penny would most likely drop. And if it did not, the child could at least perform the ritual!

Nowadays, 'understanding' is said to be acquired through the concrete representation of the symbolic at all stages. Thus, in order to calculate 10 × 8, the child must understand the operation; and this understanding consists precisely in the recognition that 10 × 8 may be represented as 10 sets of 8, or 10 towers of 8 bricks. Simply being able to provide a correct answer to the question 'What is ten times eight?' is no evidence at all of this understanding. Indeed, a very quick answer which clearly proceeds from memory may be taken as an indication of 'rote' learning – the very opposite of 'relational understanding'.[1] In these circumstances, it is easy to see how the next aspect of the dominant ideology became so powerful.

3. THE UNIMPORTANCE OF REPETITION AND MEMORISATION

Repetition and (to some extent) memorisation have come to assume a relatively unimportant position in terms of young children's learning. It is perceived as being far more important that children discover and explore mathematical patterns (such as the sequence of triangular numbers) than that they memorise number facts or repeat number operations (for example, by doing large numbers of repetitive 'sums'). The rationale against the practice of encouraging children to do pages of routinised arithmetic was twofold:

- It was said to be boring; as such, it was considered likely to militate against children seeing mathematics as an exciting, creative subject.

✧ It was argued that if children could do five examples correctly, there was no point in their doing a further twenty examples of a similar kind.

However, the repetition or rehearsal of particular numerical operations plays a vital function in the gaining of an automaticity in their performance. Thus doing fifty examples rather than five is a key factor in helping children to perform these operations *without thinking about them* – that is, automatically. This automatic level of functioning is a crucial aspect of later competent mathematical achievement, where it is essential that simple numerical operations are performed with ease in order to let the mind focus on the more complex mathematical functions involved at this level. We witness this lack of automaticity in many thousands of children leaving primary school today, for whom relatively simple mathematical operations (such as 72–39) become a source of much laborious thinking and difficulty.

A second important point is that it has been noted that many children (and girls in particular) actually *enjoy* doing a substantial amount of repetitive number work. Its ritual nature means that they can achieve a high level of success, and this in turn produces gains in confidence. In marked contrast, some of the investigative or problem-solving tasks produce a high level of insecurity, unhappiness or simple boredom in many children. (See Walkerdine, 1989.) Too often, they are unsure what to do or how to approach the problem, and have no strategies upon which to draw in reaching a solution. Furthermore, the lack of a degree of automaticity of skill makes it harder to achieve a familiarity with particular procedures or algorithms, which retain for a long time their feeling of strangeness or difficulty. And the last thing that one needs when attempting to solve a more complex mathematical problem or investigate a particular mathematical pattern is an insecurity with the tools of the trade.

MOVING PAST COCKCROFT

It is clearly the case that a reappraisal of this approach, and a long hard scrutiny of its effectiveness over the last ten years, is necessary. However, in conducting such an examination, we must be careful to protect the proverbial baby from being ejected with its bath water. An approach is needed which improves on the current model without reverting to the traditional one. This requires us to rethink some key aspects of our approach to the teaching and learning of mathematics. In embryo, at least, this is what I will now try to outline.

MATHS AS LANGUAGE

Firstly, we need to reassert the importance of what we have earlier termed the mental and linguistic aspects of mathematics. To some extent, this contrasts with the emphasis currently placed on physical enactment or concrete realisation. Let us tease out what we mean by 'mental and linguistic' here. This idea relates closely to the conception of mathematics as a language. As children acquire a language, they try out new terms and different grammatical constructions in advance of being able to explain fully what they mean. Thus very young children come to use terms such as 'this' and 'there', realising both how to use these terms and that their meaning is dependent upon their context – i.e. who utters them and in what circumstances. However, they could neither define these terms nor provide any account of how to use them. In this sense, *their understanding not infrequently lags behind their usage*.

As mathematics educators, we can encourage exactly the same process. Children can use certain operations in advance of their ability to explain their meaning. Thus children can recognise and predict the sequence 20, 30, 40... without necessarily being aware of the physical representation of 4 x 10 as four towers of ten or four 'rods' of Dienes blocks. Still more crucially, children may well be able to count correctly the sequence of numbers 86, 87, 88, 89, 90; provide all the numbers between 85 and 89; and correctly identify which numbers are one more or two more than 86; without being in a position to explain to a third party the significance of the '8' digit relative to the '6' digit in 86. In other words, there are many important number skills which may precede an understanding of place value; arguably, such an understanding may be developed precisely through the exercise of these number skills.

What is being claimed here is that, in some important respects, learning maths and developing a series of mathematical competencies is more like learning a language than has previously been acknowledged. To demand 'understanding' in the sense that the child can *explain* the meaning of what he or she is doing, often in relation to some concrete realisation with bricks or base ten equipment, is to miss the point and, sometimes, to slow down the learner and impede the learning process. With maths, as with language, children should be encouraged to *use* their mathematical skills and improve their mathematical techniques repeatedly, as well as developing new ones. In this way, as they use the mathematics, they will come to understand (and possibly to explain) why what they are doing works, and thus to provide an account of its *meaning*.

MATHEMATICAL MEANING

The notion of mathematical meaning is of crucial importance to us as teachers. It is worth teasing out exactly what we expect when we ask a child, in mathematics, what something means. If we ask a child 'What does $27 \div \square = 3$ mean?', there are three possible answers to that question which would indicate that the child has made some sense of that number sentence. These answers can be categorised as three different ways of 'reading' a mathematical expression:

1. *It can be read syntactically*. This interprets the question 'What does this mean?' as a 'How do you do this?' question. 'Well, you divide the 3 into the 27 and you get 9. The answer is 9.' The question is treated in a purely operational sense: the child does with the number sentence what is required in the context. She or he reads it precisely as an operation, and performs that operation. This reading will therefore only be possible if the child has a strategy for performing the relevant number operation.

2. *It can be read semantically*. This interprets the question 'What does this mean?' as a request for a paraphrase. Possible answers include "Well, it means 27 divided by something is 3' or 'What do you have to divide 27 by to get an answer of 3?' or 'How many threes are there in twenty-seven?' The interpretation of the request for meaning as a suggestion that they should try to find another way of saying the same thing involves treating the number sentence exactly as if it were any other English sentence. The child rephrases the number sentence,

putting it into words rather than using symbols. This reading may well generate a strategy for finding the solution, and it may also make clear to the teacher the strategies (e.g. counting in threes) and the techniques (e.g. using a number grid) which are necessary for the child to be able to perform the relevant operation.

3. *It can be read as a symbolic representation of a physical state of affairs*. 'It means that you count out 27 bricks and then you share them among some people and each person gets three.' In this instance, the child looks to realise the number sentence as a physical state of affairs, using concrete materials such as bricks. This particular answer involves only one of many possible realisations; but it may also, in this particular case, assist the child in finding a solution.

However, the usefulness of this third reading is qualified. Some concrete realisations may help children to get an answer, while others will not. And some may actually inhibit the process of performing the operation satisfactorily. In 'reading' $3 \times 5 = \square$, it may be helpful to produce a physical representation: 'Three towers of five cubes' gives a way of finding the answer. But take another example: $49 \div 7 = \square$. In getting to grips with this number sentence, the reading 'Forty-nine divided by seven is...' followed by the paraphrase 'How many sevens are there in forty-nine?' is undoubtedly a more helpful reading than the more concrete 'Forty-nine bricks shared among seven people is how many each?' We do not want children to approach the problem $49 \div 7 = \square$ by having to count out 49 bricks and share these among 7 people. We do on the other hand, require that children read the division $49 \div 7 = \square$ as 'How many sevens in forty-nine?', since this not only supplies a reading of the number sentence (arguably indicating an understanding of its meaning) but also indicates an appropriate strategy for finding the answer.

This argument leads us to the view that instead of thinking about whether children 'understand' what they are doing in maths, we would do better to think in terms of whether children can make appropriate 'readings'. This view relies upon the conception of maths as a language, and allows us to draw useful parallels between 'reading' an English sentence (whether in print or orally) and 'reading' a number sentence.

READING MATHS

The first question we, as teachers, want to ask children as we present them with simple mathematical formulations is 'Can you read these sentences?' Thus, presented with examples like:

$$4 + 3 = \square \qquad 7 \times 8 = \square \qquad 57 - \square = 20$$

we want to be reassured that children can supply us with a range of readings, such as:

> Four and three makes...
>
> Seven times eight is...
>
> Fifty-seven take away something leaves twenty.

We may then want to probe these readings further: 'What does *times* mean?' – we will be looking for an answer such as 'It means seven lots of eight.'

In addressing these mathematical sentences as *sentences* which require *reading*, we are focusing less on the child's understanding, and more on the performative aspects of these mathematical operations. Thus, in presenting children with mathematical formulations, we need to ask two questions. Firstly, can they read this? Secondly, can they find an answer? The first part requires that we enable children to acquire a real familiarity and confidence with the language of mathematics. The second requires that we offer a range of appropriate techniques or strategies to enable children to perform mathematical operations. The aim is to make children *literate* in mathematics, so that they can use its symbols and techniques fluently.

This two-stage process is summarised in Figure 2 – from which, it can clearly be seen that this approach avoids the question of whether children have really 'understood' a piece of maths by effectively bypassing the notion of 'understanding'. However, it builds in a place for physical manipulation of objects and concrete realisations of mathematical formulations – not as an end in themselves, nor as a necessary step in the production of understanding, but as *one way of*

Teacher	Child
Provides a continuous series of *readings* of mathematical statements, using constant repetition.	*Reads* the mathematical formulation (perhaps providing several readings).
Ensures that these readings are embedded in a variety of different contexts.	Recognises the sentence as it appears in the different contexts.
Suggests and provides a series of techniques by means of which children can perform the operation.	Draws upon the appropriate *techniques* or *strategies* to solve the problem or perform the operation.
Allows for the necessary rehearsal to enable a degree of automaticity of performance.	Becomes comfortable and familiar with these techniques and may then adapt or modify the given strategies to invent their own.

Figure 2

producing a reading of mathematical sentences.

A further point about this approach is the way that it accentuates the need for the provision and repetition of technical skills and strategies. One type of reading (which we have termed the syntactic reading) of mathematical problems is an operational reading, in which we simply do what is required to find a solution. Here the major requirement, in terms of skills, is that the child has at least one appropriate technique or strategy at her or his disposal. This becomes clearer if we work through an example:

$$27 + 7 = \square$$

1. Syntactic reading:

'How do I do it? Start at twenty-seven. Count on. Twenty-eight, twenty-nine, thirty, thirty-one, thirty-two, thirty-three, thirty-four.'

Strategy used: a counting-on technique.

2. Semantic reading:

'Twenty-seven and seven makes...

Twenty-seven add three is thirty, and four more is thirty-four.'

Strategy used: a number bonds/next ten recognition plus counting on.

Two strategies are used in these examples; the second is clearly more advanced than, and hence preferable to, the first. In the second, the child clearly utilises her or his knowledge of number bonds (i.e. that 7 + 3 = 10 and that 3 + 4 = 7) and recognition of the 'next ten' (i.e. that the next ten after 27 is 30). However, the child also utilises the more primary 'counting-on' technique to complete the algorithm.

Both readings are effective. They allow for, and facilitate the utilisation of, an effective strategy. However, the likelihood of a more sophisticated strategy being used is greatly increased by a semantic reading of the statement. Both readings draw upon the image of a number line, where numbers are imagined as a series and addition is conceptualised as moving along the series. Thus the *mental* model of the number line may be said to underpin both readings. This is in sharp contrast to the third reading.

> 3. Physical representation reading:
> 'Start with 27. Count out 27 bricks.
> Count out 7 more.
> Finally, count the total number.'
> Strategy used: combining two sets.

This reading requires little comment, other than to observe that although it is a strategy which no teacher would wish to encourage Year 2 children to use, it is precisely the strategy and the reading which dominate early infant work in addition. We continually 'read' addition as the combination of two sets, and have displayed a marked reluctance to read it syntactically or semantically.

It is in this sense, then, that we are concerned to shift the focus of teachers' interest from a notion of mathematical understandings to one of mathematical readings. In employing an approach which encourages, or even requires, children to 'read' mathematical sentences, it is possible to retain the idea of a physical representation (or a description of one) as one of three ways of producing a valid and useful reading. However, we argue that a specifically concrete (in the Piagetian sense) realisation is neither the only nor the most important way in which 'understanding' is produced. We also abandon the construction of a hierarchy of mathematical performances, from those where the child evinces a 'real' or 'true' understanding to those where they display only a 'rote' response. Instead, we accept that there are different possible readings of mathematical sentences; and that, in each individual case, the context coupled with the need to select an effective strategy will militate in favour of particular types of reading and against others.

CONCLUSIONS

In this chapter, we have argued for a change in the ways in which we think about teaching and learning maths. We have traced the genesis of many current (but now contested) orthodoxies in maths education, finding their origins in the Cockcroft Report and in many of the quasi-Piagetian ideas which have influenced primary education from the 1960s onwards. Particularly noteworthy was the idea that children's development proceeds in stages and that learning, in this sense, follows development.

Two implications followed from this idea. The first was that particular concepts or operations cannot be taught until the child is 'ready'. The second was that in order to understand mathematical sentences or statements, children need to be provided with a concrete realisation of these sentences. These implications have had profound and far-reaching consequences in terms of teaching approaches in maths. Because children are not felt to be 'ready', infant teachers in particular have been wary of introducing large numbers, counting above 10 or 20, or working with some of the more abstract operations such as doubling and halving. Also, the insistence on linking something called 'understanding' to concrete realisations has, in practice, greatly reduced the reliance in teaching upon the building-up of mental models and the production of habitual mathematical routines, (such as counting in tens).

There is now substantial and mounting evidence (see the TIMSS Reports, 1996) that children's competencies and attainments in maths in the U.K. are not at a level commensurate either with those of children in other, comparable, societies or with those of children in the U.K. 20 years ago. In the face of this evidence, we have suggested that we need to find new ways of underpinning our teaching, and of construing and describing what happens in the teaching and learning of mathematics.

We have suggested that maths, rather than being conceived as a body of knowledge (a bundle of facts and procedures), can be described as being like a language. Many of the techniques that children apply to the learning of language can equally well be applied to their learning of mathematics. In place of the vexed notion of mathematical understanding, we have suggested that children are required to produce plausible *readings* of mathematical statements. Thus, faced with any formulation or symbolic construction in maths, children can be asked 'What does this say?' In response, they may produce a variety of possible readings.

One of the most powerful strategies I have observed and used as a teacher is to ask one child 'What does this say?' and follow this up by asking a second child 'What did she say it meant?', then asking a third 'Is that correct?' and a fourth 'What do *you* think it means?' Demanding, and being prepared to offer, a series of readings of mathematical expressions helps children to make sense of the maths they are doing. They construct meanings in the course of using their mathematics, as they do in everyday language. And the construction of meaning is a *social* process, involving dialogue and discussion.

We have argued that this idea of a variety of different readings has a number of advantages. Firstly, it allows children to make different *interpretations*. The notion of interpretations is a very useful one in maths. Because an interpretation is an act, we can look at it, make comments and give the child a chance to improve it. This contrasts with the notion of 'understanding': we cannot look at a child's understanding of something, since an understanding is by nature invisible and we can only access it indirectly. Studying a child's interpretation of a mathematical sentence, we can not only see how valid it is, but also use it diagnostically. Looking at how children interpret different mathematical formulations will give us a real insight into how they are thinking and the types of mistake they may be likely to make.

Secondly, the idea that children *read* maths returns us to a notion of semantics and syntax, at the same time as shifting the emphasis from an exclusive focus on concrete representations. To see the sense they are making of their readings, and to help them develop possible new readings, we need to provide children with *mental* models – metaphors by which we think. These include very powerful models such as the number line and the 0–99 number square. Developing a reliance upon these models is a crucial step in the development of mental mathematical skills. (A parallel might be drawn with the use of symbolic materials such as maps and diagrams in the teaching of other subjects.)

Thirdly, some of the children's readings of mathematical statements will be syntactic, and will require and presuppose the existence of a set of *strategies* for performing an operation. Through the construction of a series of mental models, teachers can focus on providing specific strategies, by means of which the children can carry out operations. For example, the child may use the model of a number line to arrive at the strategy of counting on when performing an addition. Children may then require a *technique* to enable them to apply this strategy in a particular case. For example, in trying to count on, they may use fingers or a number line. Either of these is a technique which enables them to use the strategy of counting on.

The emphasis on strategies and techniques not only returns us to the realm of mental models, it also provides a specific and appropriate place for repetition and routinised practice, both oral and written. Children develop their mental fluency in mathematics, as they develop their fluency in any language, through *using* the strategies and techniques. As Wittgenstein observed, the meaning of a word is its use. We could say that reading mathematics is being able to use it.

NOTES

1. See Skemp, R. (1971)*The Psychology of Learning Mathematics* for an elaboration of the difference between relational understanding and rote understanding.

CHAPTER 4

NUMERACY AND CALCULATORS

INTRODUCTION

Over the last twenty years, there has been a great deal of excitement about the humble four-function calculator, and much speculation about how it might force a rethink of the curriculum for mathematics in the primary school. It is fair to say that the revolution has not yet come! There are a good many reasons for this, and some have to do with a failure to appreciate that the presence of the machines in classrooms is not in itself sufficient to influence the quality of children's learning. It is now apparent that any account of the place of calculators in primary education must include discussion of:

- approaches to calculation in general, and mental methods in particular;
- teaching styles which challenge children's thinking and promote their intellectual independence.

A calculation can be performed in one or more of three basically different ways: mentally, with pencil and paper, or with a calculator. The third of these options has been available for a mere blink of time in the long history of arithmetic. Electronic reckoning differs from the other means of calculation in a number of respects. For example, complex calculations such as 276×467 are, in principle, no more 'difficult' to execute with a calculator than trivial ones such as 2×3. There is a very real and obvious sense in which responsibility for the technical details of the actual calculation are delegated and entrusted to the 'black box', a machine which accepts our input and responds with an output.

It is therefore hardly surprising that the use of such machines should commonly be viewed as inconsistent with the rational training of young minds. If, as we believe, the calculator is a very considerable asset for developing numeracy in the primary classroom, its potential is widely misunderstood and largely unrealised. In this chapter, we will review the background to the current situation, survey some related research and curriculum development, and make some proposals for school policy and classroom practice.

NUMERACY, CALCULATORS AND CALCULATIONS

Calculators are not exactly new on the scene. The world's first electronic hand-held calculator was announced in Tokyo by Canon Business Machines in April 1970. Such a machine cost about £50 in 1973, but by the mid-1970s Sinclair were marketing a truly pocket-sized calculator in the U.K. for around £10. Within a couple of years, HMI Michael Girling (1977) could observe that 'a cheap calculator can be bought for the price of two good cabbages'.

Girling offered a radical, new definition of numeracy:

> Basic numeracy is the ability to use a four-function electronic calculator sensibly.

It is all the more remarkable that Girling was writing in the context of a period in which the 'back to basics' movement had gained some attention and influence. In the light of his definition, Girling set out an agenda for curriculum development in school mathematics, including:

- sensible use of calculators;
- the place of mental calculations;
- use of algorithms;
- investigation of patterns in number.

These ideas were developed by our former colleague Stuart Plunkett (1979) in an article which continues to be influential in the minds of those – in Britain and around the world (McIntosh et al, 1995) – who address Girling's agenda. Plunkett argued that standard written algorithms tend to militate against understanding, whereas mental algorithms invariably require understanding:

> I think that the reasons for teaching the standard written algorithms are out of date, and that it is time we all took notice of

> this. I believe there is a place for mental algorithms, for the use of calculators, and for ad hoc, non-standard written methods.

By 1982, the Cockcroft Report had gently refuted the back-to-basics approach and endorsed Girling's train of thought:

> We believe that the decline of mental and oral work within mathematics classrooms represents a failure to recognise the central place which working 'done in the head' occupies throughout mathematics (para. 255).
>
> In our view, more [development work] is needed both to consider the use of calculators as an aid to teaching and learning... and also the extent to which the arithmetical aspects of the curriculum may need to be modified (para. 388).

In the U.K. the ideological ground had been laid for a bold experiment in calculator innovation.

THE CAN PROJECT

The Cockcroft Report had pointed to the need for developmental work which would take into account the technological and social changes of the previous two decades, and draw on the resources of research and development which had become available. In 1985, the School Curriculum Development Committee approved a proposal for a major four-year primary mathematics project (subsequently named Primary Initiatives in Mathematics Education, or PrIME) to be directed by Hilary Shuard at Homerton College, Cambridge. PrIME aimed 'to help teachers to carry out the recommendations of the Cockcroft Report, taking account of the impact of the new technology' (SCDC, 1986), with a comprehensive agenda including language in mathematical thought and learning, mathematical investigations and problem solving, the role of practical work, teaching styles, classroom organisation, gender, culture and the role of parents. While PrIME is best remembered for CAN, the component associated with developing the use of calculators, it is worth bearing in mind that CAN was only one item in a complex network of curriculum development issues.

CAN (Calculator-Aware Number Curriculum) envisaged a classroom environment which would take full account of the possibilities opened up by calculators, each child having free access to one, and integrated the use of calculators in classroom activities of all kinds. It is important to remember that CAN was set up first and foremost as a curriculum development project, not as a research study. The principal aim of CAN was to bring about a change in primary school mathematics on a national scale. There was little systematic (as opposed to anecdotal) evaluation of the effect of the CAN curriculum on the children and teachers involved in it. Nevertheless, a study of the early stages of CAN in one LEA (Rowland, 1994) noted that six- to seven-year-old children exposed to a calculator-aware number curriculum tended to develop early familiarity with large numbers and efficient methods for mental calculation for numbers less than 100. This study also noted that involvement in CAN had caused some teachers to revise upwards their expectations of what young children could do and understand in school mathematics.

However, Rowland also observed that the least able children (in mainstream classes) seemed not to benefit from their access to calculators. This was disputed by some CAN teachers, who claimed that they had at least noticed an improved *attitude* to mathematics in these children. The CAN team's national evaluator concluded (Duffin, 1993) that the project had influenced the mathematics curriculum, developed an investigative teaching style and empowered children. The 'authorised' CAN report (Shuard et al, 1991) is predictably upbeat.

In addition to these positive impressions of the CAN experience, there is (somewhat fortuitously) some data which enables a CAN-control comparison to be made. Suffolk, as one of the original English Partner Authorities in the project, provided four schools where the CAN approach was pioneered from September 1986. At that time, Suffolk children were routinely tested in mathematics at the ages of eight plus and twelve plus on instruments created for the LEA from an NFER (National Foundation for Educational Research) item bank

– thus providing data which could be used for a comparison. In February 1989, the LEA compared the results of that year's CAN cohort of 116 children with a randomly selected group of 116 pupils from other schools in the county (Oram, 1989). So far as we are aware, this remains the only published attempt to make a quantitative comparison between CAN project and non-project children – though its findings must be interpreted with caution, because of the difficulties in obtaining matched samples in such studies. Nevertheless, the results certainly appear striking.

The test consisted of 36 items, most of them concerned with the understanding of number and place value. Of the 36, CAN children scored higher than the comparison group on 26 items. The comparison group scored more highly on six items; on the other four there was no difference. It is also worth noting the margin of difference between the two groups: where the comparison group scored higher, it was by a small percentage only (highest 4.3%); where the CAN group scored higher, it was by margins of up to 30%. On 11 items, the CAN group's facility rate was higher by more than 10%. The most striking example was test item 10 (see Figure 1).

Figure 1

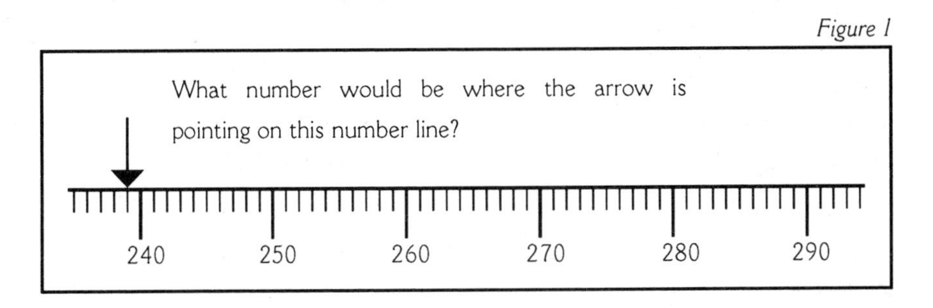

74.1% of the CAN children were successful on this item, compared with 44% of the control group. Not all of the items where CAN children scored better were pure number: others concerned measurement, shape and reading a scale. One hypothesis put forward by CAN teachers to explain this was that the children were more able to attach meaning to numbers in measurement and other contexts than they had been before CAN.

Although well aware of the exciting reports coming from the CAN project, the working group who wrote the original National Curriculum for England and Wales (DES, 1989) were divided about the place of calculators. Despite the inevitable compromises, their curriculum endorsed calculators as a learning tool to an extent previously undreamed of in the majority of primary classrooms. The splendid Section E of the Non-Statutory Guidance to Mathematics in the National Curriculum (DES, 1989) is entirely positive about the contribution of calculators to the learning of mathematics in the primary years. The effect of this was that the machines became commonplace in primary schools, because teachers had received the message that calculators had official sanction and were therefore a 'good thing'. Actual *enthusiasm* for them, however, is still extremely variable, and so is their effective availability to children. CAN children had virtually free access to the machines, and developed their ideas about number partly through using them. Without this level of access, children in most schools appear not to be developing sufficient familiarity with their use to cross a 'threshold' of competence beyond which the calculator is used as a genuine tool for exploration and experimentation with numbers.

INTERNATIONAL COMPARISONS

Comparative surveys (Lapointe et al, 1992; Foxman, 1992; OFSTED, 1994) confirm anecdotal impressions that the use of calculators in British schools is more extensive than elsewhere. Most other countries take a conservative, cautious approach to calculators in primary education, consistent with the view that numeracy is best developed through computational fluency and without a calculator. (This is especially notable in the Pacific Rim countries that made them affordable elsewhere!) There are a few qualified exceptions: CAN-type projects have been started since the late 1980s in Australia, California, South Africa and elsewhere – though they vary in the details and style of their approach, particularly as regards the teaching (or not) of standard algorithms.

Calculator research in the USA has tended to focus on children who had *already formed* their number knowledge in conventional ways, and who were 'exposed' to calculators for short periods ranging from one lesson to one term of about 30 days (see, for example, Hembree and Dessart, 1986, 1992). While such studies (as summarised in the Cockcroft Report: 'use of calculators has not produced any adverse effect on computational ability'), can reassure the cautious they give little positive encouragement.

In Australia, the Calculators in Primary Mathematics project, which began in 1990, is a long-term investigation into the effects of calculators on maths teaching and learning in primary schools. The project has much in common with CAN, as well as a more systematic research base for evaluation purposes. Findings from the project support the belief that free access to calculators enhances learning. For example, Susie Groves (1994) reports a study in which a sample of over 50 nine- to ten-year-old 'project children' were interviewed about their approach to 24 computational items. Their responses were compared with those of a matched sample of non-project pupils. The performance of the project group was significantly better than that of the control group. For example, on the item 62 750 + 50 (presented on a card), the facility rates for the two groups were: project 89%, control 56%. Interestingly, 22% of the control group resorted to a calculator for this item, compared with only 16% of those who had had three years' free access to calculators at school!

It is fascinating to note the current enthusiasm for so-called 'continental' teaching methods in mathematics (Neumark, 1996). These methods are characterised by a more teacher-led style than that presumed to exist in the majority of British classrooms, with heavy emphasis on interactive class teaching and mental calculations. When those methods are examined, however, the similarities with the way in which CAN forced many British teachers to operate are striking. Pupils explaining and justifying to the rest of the class their own methods of working, structured activities designed to provoke cognitive challenge, startling mental calculation ability, a sense of ownership and control of methods – these features are all reminiscent of CAN classrooms. Most significantly, both CAN and 'continental' teaching styles oblige teachers to *engage in meaningful communication with children about the mathematics under consideration*, something which can be avoided almost completely by teachers who are happy to rely exclusively upon a commercial mathematics scheme.

But as we have noted, another aspect of 'continental methods' is the total absence of calculators. Our view is that, far from being at opposite poles, CAN and the 'continental' approach have much in common; and a judicious blending of the two might offer the best of both worlds.

DEVELOPING NUMERACY WITH CALCULATORS

Further research is needed to clarify the specific advantages which integrated calculator use confers on children. Kenneth Ruthven and Laurie Rousham are currently conducting such a study in Cambridge, supported by the ESRC. One of the questions is that raised by Pea (1985) and Dörfler (1993) about whether the calculator is capable of acting as a 'cognitive reorganiser' as well as a 'cognitive amplifier'. The latter term refers to the often-cited advantage of calculators in enabling children to handle data which would otherwise be beyond their computational reach (for example, larger or more 'messy' numbers). In this way, the machine is acting like any tool which extends the user's reach, just as a socket wrench amplifies the torque which we can apply to turning a nut.

A potentially much more interesting function of calculators is as a cognitive *reorganiser* which allows (or even obliges) the user to experience, and thus conceptualise, number in a different way. This seems to happen in two ways:

✧ Firstly, a *feedback loop* (Rousham, 1995) is set up through the interaction of a primarily symbolic device (the calculator) with the learner's pre-existing knowledge. Young children experimenting with a series of calculations (such as $28 \times 4 + 14 \div 3 - 32 = 10$) notice that the calculator effectively keeps a 'running total' on its display (e.g. by carrying out the multiplication by 4 as soon as the addition sign is pressed.) The calculator thus offers information along the way which would normally be ignored by someone who was interested only in arriving quickly at a final answer. Children are capable of taking this unsolicited 'feedback' and incorporating it into their decision about what to do next: in the example, the child was attempting to 'make ten'; so when the machine displays 126 (which it does as soon as the division sign is pressed) the operator can look at the total before deciding which number to divide by. This feedback information allows an active process of constructing new knowledge about numbers and operations, while not imposing imagery upon it.

✧ Secondly, by releasing the user from low-level tasks (correct computations), the calculator may free up cognitive 'space' which can thus be devoted to higher-order tasks – such as monitoring how the problem is proceeding and deciding which operation needs to be carried out next - thereby providing a context for children to exercise cognitive functions which were hitherto the province only of the most able and mathematically confident.

Anecdotal evidence suggests that children who have used calculators sufficiently to cross a 'threshold' of competence (see page 66 above) gain in confidence, but do not become dependent upon the machines. It is children who have been taught that they should not really be using them at all, and whose mathematical confidence is not good, who are most at risk of developing uncritical dependence. Perhaps unfortunately, the calculator is of very limited use to those who turn to it as a lifejacket because they are drowning in a sea of half-remembered rules and concepts. The evidence suggests, paradoxically, that *more* calculator use and not less is the answer to fears of dependency. Susie Groves (1994, p.38) provides further evidence in support of this conclusion.

MAKING PROGRESS

We believe that despite hostility to calculator use from the media, some parents and a few educators, there exists a real desire among British primary teachers to make better use of them. In this section, we offer six practical suggestions about how this might be achieved within a school.

That calculators are present in almost every British school is largely a result of the prominence given to them by the original National Curriculum document. That the quality of use of these calculators is generally disappointing can be ascribed to many factors, but is attested to by a number of studies (Warren & Ling 1994, OFSTED

1994). It is common to find that the machines are kept in cupboards, are not really accessible to pupils except at individual teachers' discretion, and are brought out only infrequently for low-level purposes such as the checking of calculations done by other means.

Despite this, we do not consider the position to be hopeless. A considerable INSET investment would be required to bring all primary teachers to a fuller realisation of the usefulness of the calculator as a tool for teaching and learning. But where the motivation exists, much can be done at the individual level. Many adults, including teachers, have not yet familiarised themselves with the calculator in everyday life. Teachers have had to become familiar with computers; the amount of time and INSET effort required for this, both inside and outside the classroom, is generally recognised. Calculators are far more widely available, but far more lowly regarded.

Are you a confident calculator user? Try this real-life problem. You fill your car's petrol tank and zero the trip recorder. After 358 miles, you put in a further 41.9 litres to bring the tank back to full again. The information that a litre is 0.22 of a gallon is available to you on the station forecourt. You have a calculator in your glovebox in order to work out how economical your car is. What calculations do you need to make before you move off and zero the recorder again, in order to work out that the car's economy is 38.8 miles per gallon?

What is important here is not the ability to carry out calculations to several decimal places – the machine will do that for you. What you need is that detached grasp of the structure of the situation which allows you to interpret the display and decide what to do next. Are you going to divide – if so what, and by what? To multiply? Similar questions apply. You need to know what you are doing and why; and that there may be more than one way to get the correct answer. Happily, the speed of the calculator means that you can utilise the 'feedback loop' by simply trying out several possible calculations in turn – provided that you can use common sense to evaluate the answer obtained. Whatever operations you employ, it will be necessary to judge the reasonableness of the answer. This is similar to the situation we are trying to put children in as they deal with much simpler problems: along the way, they should be noticing the effects of carrying out different types of operation and routinely comparing the results with what they were expecting. This is the beginning of intelligent calculator use.

Accordingly, our first recommendation would be:

1. In order to become a confident calculator user, carry a calculator and use it frequently.

Where school policy and classroom practice are concerned, the experience of the CAN schools may be inspirational – but it also has some features which are not easily replicable. In particular, the teachers involved enjoyed sustained and funded professional encouragement from their LEAs and from the PrIME project. Similarly, those participating in the Australian calculator project are provided with systematic professional support. Nor can one dismiss the so-called Hawthorne effect on participants in special projects: mere participation seems to enhance performance.

Therefore, in presenting five further suggestions intended as a possible model for practice and progress in any school or classroom, we draw upon our experience of research into calculator use in many classrooms (some in post-CAN schools, some not). The intention is to work towards *an overall strategy which embraces and integrates calculator use*, and thus the suggestions will work much better if they are discussed, modified as appropriate and then implemented by a whole-school staff (or at least a teaching team), rather than being the initiative of a solitary teacher.

Once you have become a confident calculator user yourself, aware of its useful features, strengths and limitations, the next step is this:

2. Give your children real access to calculators, so that they can cross the 'threshold' and use the machine as an experimental, exploratory tool.

In our experience, you may well have to encourage or even enforce use of the calculator at first, so powerful in many children's minds is the idea that using a calculator is somehow 'wrong', or 'cheating'. This will be lessened, of course, if they see *you* using one. It will take time before calculator usage is familiar enough for it to become an investigative tool. Do not be disappointed if you introduce calculators and see no exciting results at first. It will help if you:

3. Regularly provide the children with purposeful activities, some of which would be difficult or impossible to do without the machines.

Some of these activities should be structured ones intended to provoke cognitive challenge, mathematical discussion and learning. For example, ask the whole class to write down a list of 25 numbers, some big, some small, some decimals and so on. Then say: 'This table, multiply all the numbers in your list by ten. This table, add zero to all your numbers. This table, add ten to them all. This table, multiply them all by one [or zero, or twenty]...'.

As the children compare their input and output numbers, they will begin to tell you that they don't need the calculator to do these things. They will also be discovering things about how the number system works. But in addition to activities which are fairly tightly structured by the teacher, it is important to include some which are more open-ended and 'creative', such as asking them to make up a long string of calculations which ends up with the answer 10. For a fuller discussion of the structured/creative distinction and further examples of each, see Rousham (1995); for a wealth of good calculator activities with examples of children's work, see Shuard et al (1991). The London-based BEAM project publishes some good calculator resource material (such as Lewis, 1993) for work with children, parents and other teachers. So our next recommendation is that you:

4. Encourage experimentation with calculators and discussion of children's observations when they experiment.

Calculators are not primarily in the classroom to do sums, and their use must not be restricted to the checking of calculations already carried out by other means – which is sterile and undermines the rationale for much school mathematics. Children will think, 'If we're going to have to check the accuracy of our answers with a calculator anyway, what is the point in learning to do it the hard way?' View the calculator not just as a device to carry out calculations, but as another piece of maths apparatus, with a distinctive ability to illustrate and uncover the structure of the number system and how it works.

The goal of this increased familiarity with the number system –

what Hilary Shuard called 'a friendly feeling for numbers' – is better mental calculation. So to the next recommendation.

5. Promote mental calculation as the first resort.

Research such as that of Fitzgerald (1985) shows that as adults, we tend to look at a calculation and do it in our heads if we can: if we cannot, perhaps because the numbers are too big (or too small) or it would take too long, then we use a calculator. What we very seldom do nowadays is to employ the written algorithms or pencil and paper methods that we were taught in school. Wherever maths has to be done in the real world, it is being done with the aid of calculating tools of one kind or another. Mental calculation is increasingly important within this scenario, written methods much less so.

Part of the basis for objection to calculator use in primary schools is that adults use calculators to get out of doing maths. CAN showed that children use them to get *into* doing maths – at least if they are given sufficient experience and encouragement to do so.

If you put into practice the suggestions we have made so far, there will be some changes in the children's work. Almost inevitably, this will have an effect on your teaching style. You will have to:

6. Expect and accept the changes which are bound to result from calculator use.

The teacher has to engage in greater discussion with the children about what the calculator is doing and what the various displays mean, and deal with their exposure to decimals and negative numbers: *respond* to work initiated by the children, almost as much as initiating work for them. In this process, some control over content will inevitably pass from the teacher to the children. If you give calculators to a class of six-year-olds, for example, you will hardly be able to restrict them to numbers below 50! They take some time to realise this, but once they do the effects will be powerful. Alan Parr, a pioneering Mathematics Inspector in Hertfordshire, asked a class of infants how many had their own calculator at home. Over twenty hands went up. 'And what do you do with them?' he asked.

Paul, aged six and nine months, said 'I do experiments on mine.'

'What sort of experiments?' enquired Alan.

Glancing furtively around, Paul answered: 'I see what happens when I multiply numbers by 99!'

Initially, such changes can be unsettling; to some teachers, even threatening. But if we can accept change gracefully, the reward is the sense of ownership and pride that children can come to display in their own mathematical abilities – that confidence in, and fierce enthusiasm for, number work which is often sadly absent when we read between the lines of OFSTED reports and Government surveys. We conclude this section with the words of a Year 6 teacher in a school which has followed a systematic programme to implement the spirit of the recommendations we have made above. Calculators are now in everyday use:

> The calculators are always available. We found so many things you could do with them that got the children thinking and got you into talking to them about what they were doing. They've made a big difference to my teaching of decimals, for instance. Sometimes we stipulate that they can't use them, and say 'We are looking at your ability to work these out in your head today', but otherwise they just use them like they would a protractor.
>
> We all found it difficult to change our approach – but we've all gone together. Talk about and evaluate activities. Talk about and try out each other's. We talk about how things went. It has taken a lot of practice. This approach is harder as a teacher – but we see that it has helped the SAT results because it makes children think of what skills to use . . . we've gone for a balance of investigative maths plus ability-based number work – and it's worked.

There is no one absolutely successful approach to mathematics teaching, but the opportunities offered by cheap and reliable calculator technology demand consideration of this kind by all schools.

CONCLUSION

In writing about the potential of integrated calculator use for enhancing mathematics learning in primary schools, we are inevitably influenced by our own involvement in the CAN project (as a teaching headteacher, and as researchers). It was always Hilary Shuard's intention that CAN should be the 'experiment' which demonstrated what she fervently believed: that free access to calculators from the outset in schools would help children to become exceptional mathematical thinkers. It is apparent that Hilary succeeded in convincing a great many people, most of whom had no direct involvement in the project itself; and calculator-aware practice continues to be held up as a way to liberate and nourish 'emergent' mathematicians.

Yet, as with computers, it is not sufficient to place the hardware in classrooms. We (the authors!) have perhaps been too slow to appreciate just how much support and guidance is needed to help teachers use calculators in ways that will promote and develop independent mathematical thinking in children. The particular support and sense of being 'special' which the CAN project teachers enjoyed is, regrettably, not available to all.

A great deal of anecdotal evidence, and a small amount of rigorous comparative research, suggests that free access to a calculator can help children to make sense of numbers: their representation, their sizes, and how they can be used to solve problems. This can be understood (in part) by seeing the calculator as having the potential both to *amplify* and to *reorganise* mathematical thinking. These aspects are interconnected, and both relate to the complex process whereby children learn by interpreting experience – by constructing a personal framework of understanding.

Functioning as a cognitive amplifier, the calculator extends the range of the data to which the child has access. To take one example, the problem 'Find two numbers whose sum is 70 and whose product is 901' becomes amenable to trial and improvement, leading to possible conjectures about how the closeness of two numbers (with a fixed sum) is related to the size of their product.

In the past, we have noted (Rowland, 1990) the reluctance of many CAN children to use structured number apparatus with which they were already familiar, and seen this as evidence of cognitive reorganisation. More recently, we have been fascinated by many children's cogent interpretation of the screen display when they input 1 ÷ 4, 2 ÷ 4, 3 ÷ 4 ... (and similarly with other constant divisors). Such activities are clearly a means of establishing a secure framework of meaning for numbers. The calculator consistently demonstrates mathematical structures and rules about how numbers are represented and how they behave. However, *it does not impose on the user any specific form of concrete imagery with which to think about numbers*. Thus the children have the maximum intellectual freedom to set each new experience with a calculator alongside their other experiences, and thus to construct, modify and add to their own frameworks of meaning.

However much we might wish it, few children embark on such explorations spontaneously once the novelty of the machine has worn off. The teacher needs to build up a repertoire of tasks such as those mentioned above, to offer them to children at appropriate moments, and then to be curious about how the children make sense of them. This last requirement underpins the requirement of *talking about mathematics* in the calculator-aware classroom, especially pupil-teacher dialogue. The accumulation of fertile calculator activities is readily achievable: they already exist in the minds and on the bookshelves of most mathematics co-ordinators. It is apparent, however, that many teachers need sustained encouragement and support within their schools, and through course attendance, to implement the suggestions we have proposed. Until they do, the calculator will remain a mere checking device.

CHAPTER 5

NUMBER OPERATIONS AND PROCEDURES

HISTORICAL BACKGROUND

A dictionary definition of an algorithm is:

> a rule for solving a mathematical problem in a finite number of steps.

Any history of algorithms has to make reference to the number systems of non-European cultures, including Babylonian, Hindu and Arabic systems. The Indian system of ten numerals (including zero) was transmitted via the Arabs to Europe, where its use became general in the twelfth century. But the mental and written algorithms based on this number system were widely resisted, and calculations were more often performed using physical methods such as counting boards.

Some of the algorithms we use today were developed much later, in the wake of the Industrial Revolution and the social changes which occurred at that time. With the advent of large factories came the need for large numbers of clerks to record finances. It became important not only that these clerks *performed* the necessary arithmetic operations, but that they could be *monitored*. Thus, whereas previously it had been sufficient to know that a designated employee (or the employer) could calculate with precision, it was now necessary to see *how* these calculations were performed in order to monitor them. Therefore a series of algorithms was devised, not for the purpose of performing the arithmetic operation, but for the purpose of checking its performance. Included in this category are many of our own most commonly used or taught algorithms, such as decomposition and long multiplication.

The fact that these algorithms have their origins not in the need to do arithmetic, but in the requirement that it should be possible to monitor others doing it, is highly relevant when we come to consider which skills these algorithms require and develop, and how these skills connect with the development of mental algorithms. In an age of computers, calculators and databases, the practical necessity for this type of monitoring has all but vanished. It is certainly arguable that a sensible pedagogy would reconsider the wisdom of teaching particular algorithms, and would wish to evaluate those written algorithms which have produced particular difficulties against the demand that children can perform satisfactorily at the mental as well as the written level. It is highly probable that such an evaluation would result in the abandonment of some written algorithms – decomposition being the most obvious – in favour of other, more mentally focused procedures.

PROBLEMS WITH ALGORITHMS

When we look closely at how children use written and mental algorithms in mathematics, we can see that there are a number of common problems. There is an increasing and reliable bank of evidence (see Chapter 3) from researchers and practitioners to the effect that some algorithms produce rather than solve problems. What are the difficulties with some written algorithms? What problems arise from conflicts between the methods children generate for themselves and those which they are given by the teacher? How do some written algorithms run counter to the development of children's mental strategies? In order to answer these, and other questions, we can categorise the problems under three headings:

1. RECALL PROBLEMS OR 'NOW WHAT DO I DO?'

The most common type of difficulty arises when children cannot remember the procedure and have no strategy for working out what they are supposed to do. For example, Kylie is doing a subtraction 73 – 45. She writes down:

$$\begin{array}{r} 73 \\ -\ 45 \\ \hline \end{array}$$

and then confesses, 'I know you're supposed to cross something out, but I can't remember what you do after that!' Kylie has a vague memory of a procedure, and she has got as far as producing the correct layout, but she cannot remember any more and is stuck for ideas.

There are at least two possible solutions to this difficulty. The first – sometimes overlooked by those maths educators locked into a notion of the primacy of something called 'real' understanding (see Chapter 3) – is to practise these algorithms so that they become 'automatic' procedures. There is an analogy with driving a car or riding a bike. We need certain skills to be on 'automatic pilot' so that we no longer worry about *how* to do them, we simply have to decide *when* to do them.

In pursuit of this automaticity, teachers thirty years ago would have used small mnemonic devices to help children recall the algorithm. Thus one of the authors was taught how to perform a long multiplication using a procedure where the first instruction was 'Lay an egg', i.e. put a zero in the units column. The same author had no idea *why* she 'laid an egg', but it produced the right answer.

Clearly, any mystification of mathematics cannot be seriously advocated; but there is a genuine point here which can easily be overlooked. Children need, and draw upon, a series of resources in performing any arithmetic operation. Some of these resources may be physical (such as fingers or a number line). Some may be cognitive/mathematical, in the sense of what we usually think of as pre-requisite skills (such as number bonds or recognising the nearest ten). And some may be verbal, acting as mnemonics or as 'prompts'. The 'lay an egg' prompt is in this latter category. It is simply a verbal prompt which produces the necessary action. Useful mnemonics include 'Turn it upside down and multiply' (dividing fractions), 'Two minuses make a plus' (multiplying negative numbers), and 'Walk before you fly' (locating a point using co-ordinates).

It is worth noting that repetition and practice play an important role in the development of confident mathematicians. Children need to repeat and rehearse their use of certain procedures, so that they no longer have to think about what they are doing or why. This is the point made by those psychologists who observe the formation and utilisation of skills, and chart how automaticity is attained. It is a point also made by Helvia Bierhoff in *The Foundations of Numeracy* (1995), where she describes how continental children are often given several times as many written exercises to do as their English counterparts. She goes on to assert that there is a causal relationship between the apparently poor performance of English children on comparative tests (see the Exeter-Kassel study, 1993) and this lack of repetitive written examples in their mathematical experience.

Certainly, children who have practised sufficiently and achieved an ease of operation with an algorithm may very well forget – since it is no longer important to them – why the algorithm works in the first place. But – as with scientific formulae in later work – this does not imply that the children have not made sense of the calculation.

The second strategy for helping children who fail to recall the correct procedure is to provide them with some means of self-support. The chances of their working out what they have to do next are greatly increased if either:

- the procedure is one which they themselves 'invented' or 'discovered'; or
- it is one which *makes sense* to them.

Precisely how children come to 'make sense' of the algorithms they use, and how they are able to articulate this sense and interpret the mathematics involved, are complex and disputed matters. But few teachers would disagree that this process of 'making sense' of an algorithm involves a high level of articulation. The more children verbalise what they are doing, the more they develop a vocabulary in which to describe the mathematical process. Discussion helps the children to stay with a difficult problem and to explore it further. They are less likely to become disconnected from their mathematical problems if they can express them. This vocabulary (which in Chapter 3 is referred to as 'readings') becomes a resource upon which children can draw when they are trying to complete a particular algorithm. Articulation is a key to the successful examination of difficulty. Children do not so much need to think things through as to *talk* them through.

2. THE WRONG STRATEGY

The second type of problem arises when children have a different strategy to the one supplied – and insisted upon – by the teacher. For example, a child may perform a subtraction using equal addition rather than decomposition ('borrow and pay back'). Rounding strategies are especially likely to be used by a child who is performing the subtraction mentally (see the next section). Teachers often appear to have few alternatives to the standard division algorithm, and to be intolerant of children's invented methods.

As we see later (page xx), drawing upon different cultural ways of solving a particular set of numerical problems will supply us with an armoury of different strategies, some of which will be more suitable than others for addressing the needs of particular children. In this context, and by way of an example, we can describe a popular Russian multiplication strategy which not only focuses attention on the 'patterns' aspect of multiplication, but also provides a means of getting the right answer to a long multiplication without having to know the tables. This algorithm is not offered here as a practical alternative to teaching the more standard long multiplication algorithm; rather, it is a way of exploring how multiplication works in our number system.

325 × 14

Write down the larger number and 1.	325	1
Double both sides.	650	2
Keep going like this.	1300	4
	2600	8

When the next double will make
the number on the RHS bigger than 14, stop.
Pick the numbers on the RHS
which add up to make 14. $8 + 4 + 2 = 14$
Add their matching numbers
on the LHS. $2600 + 1300 + 650$

This gives the answer. **4550**

Children will routinely either invent their own strategy or algorithm, or adapt one which they have been taught. They may also be taught different strategies at home from those taught in school. In order to do any piece of maths successfully a child needs to know two things: first, 'Is it possible?' and second, 'Can I do it this way?' From the teacher's point of view, we have certainly learned that it is of crucial importance to accept the children's own invented or derived methods for doing something, even if these are not the methods that we teach in school. The child who comes from home with a way of doing subtraction which she has learned from Granny, and which she can do with confidence, should be encouraged to continue using that method (though she may also be introduced to alternative methods).

Research into the learning of mathematics abounds with examples of children's invented procedures and their adaptations of conventional algorithms. Certainly, when it comes to mental procedures, we all fall back on our own tried and tested methods – even where these are not necessarily the best or the most efficient way of getting an answer. In the choice of an algorithm, reliability and accuracy are often more important than speed.

However, the evidence of both current research and current practice suggests that children need to be offered 'global' arithmetic strategies and the mental models which enable them to develop these for their own purposes. One such 'global' strategy is 'counting on', and the mental model which underpins it is that of the number line. Thus, to enable children to perform subtractions in their heads, we may suggest that they 'count on' rather than 'take away'. This means that presenting them with $45 - 27 = \square$ is less helpful than presenting them with $27 + \square = 45$. The strategy of counting on from 27 to 45 is predicated upon the realisation that we are looking for the *difference* between 27 and 45. This is the method known as 'shopkeeper's addition'. We shall return later in this chapter to the idea that children need mental models in order to help them develop mental procedures.

3. MENTAL VERSUS WRITTEN

The third problem which children often encounter in their attempts to perform a particular written algorithm is that they have a mental procedure which 'interferes' with it, or a partly learned written algorithm which is interfering with a previously secure mental procedure. A clear example of this is commonly observed when children move from infant to the junior school and start learning how to do two-figure addition as a written procedure. At Key Stage 1, children have been able to do calculations of the type 48 + 23 = ❑ by a process which involves counting on in tens and then adding on the units. The strategy used is counting on (first in tens, then in ones), and the underlying image is very much that of the number line. By contrast, in the juniors, children are often introduced to the vertical layout and written method for completing the same type of addition:

```
TU
36
27
——
——
```

They are required to add the units first, 'carry' a ten, then add the tens. The underlying image is that of base ten equipment, or coins which represent the tens and units. When utilising this algorithm, children commonly fail to read the sum. Thus they have no idea what two numbers they are adding; and if they happen to make a numerical error and achieve an answer which is unreasonable, they are totally unaware of this.

It is also often the case that the introduction of this written algorithm confuses children so that they fail to see the point of the vertical addition procedure. Last year, one of the authors observed several children completing a page of vertical additions, with base ten equipment available to them. They were found to be adding the numbers successfully in their heads: 'Thirty-six and twenty makes fifty-six, and seven more ... Well, four more is sixty, so that's sixty-three.' They would then write in 63 in the correct place for the answer. They then spent some time discussing and puzzling over where to put the '1' (i.e. the 'carry' digit) that the teacher had told them to put in!

There seemed to the researcher to be a real difficulty here. The children had a perfectly good method, with which they were confident and which made sense to them, and they were being asked to abandon it for a new and apparently 'harder' method. They were being introduced to some new maths, and the teacher was unaware of the interaction between what the children already knew and what they needed to know next. Realising their difficulty (once the researcher had pointed it out), the teacher set the children additions which involved four or five two-digit numbers. The children no longer had a simple mental strategy to perform these additions, and they therefore put some effort into making the easier, written algorithm on offer work for them in this context.

The difficulty faced by new users of written algorithms is that much of the routine is carried in the head and has to be triggered by, and co-ordinated with, a learned response to what is happening on paper. There is seldom any error-signalling from within the algorithm until the final answer is reached. Thus the child has to remember the procedure, carrying it in her or his head at the same time as performing any arithmetic operations (such as adding a string of single-digit numbers) mentally. And there is normally no indication of an error, either in the mental arithmetic or in the procedure, until the child reaches the end of the algorithm and the answer is checked for accuracy.

Furthermore, as the example above illustrates, the order in which the sub-routines of the written algorithm are carried out is unlikely to bear any relation to the mental methods which the children would use to find an answer. In this sense, the written algorithm often works against the mental methods – particularly where addition and subtraction are concerned. Thus, in moving from mental addition to written addition, children do the following:

(i) They cease to *read* the calculation to themselves. In dealing with a horizontal formulation (e.g. 46 + 37 =) children will automatically read this as *forty-six add thirty-seven* in order to proceed. Faced with the written vertical formulation of the same sum, they will begin: 'Six and seven is...'. They thus have no sense of the whole sum.

(ii) They have to remember not only the relevant number bonds,

counting on strategies and so on, but also a fixed procedure.
(iii) They are forced to abandon some of their mental strategies. For example, they would commonly deal with hundreds before tens, and tens before units, in performing any mental addition or subtraction. Using the written algorithms will almost certainly reverse this order.

Stuart Plunkett's article (1979), published in *Mathematics Teaching*, is still timely. A summary of his comments helps us to contrast mental and written algorithms (see Figure 1).

Characteristics of many standard written algorithms	Characteristics of many mental algorithms
written, fixed routines	fleeting, variable, not *designed* for recording
standardised, symbolic – operations performed directly on numerals	idiosyncratic, flexible, often iconic – referring to a number line or similar mental model
compressed, summarising	extended, modifiable – adjusted to deal with particular numbers
efficient, economic (in terms of amount of detail recorded)	active, holistic
frequently start with units, then deal with tens, etc.	largest values often dealt with first
general, exploit place value, work with any numbers	limited, specific – often relate to particular numbers and calculations (thus adding 21 to 70 may involve a different routine from that used to add 29 to 71)
do not tend to offer approximations or give a hint of what the answer will be	many provide approximations, and approximate answers appear during the algorithm

Figure 1

A striking feature of Plunkett's article is the implicit assumption that the teaching of mental methods of computation was a commonplace. The authors do not believe that this was so then, any more than it is now. Those mental arithmetic methods that are taught are often only drafted into service to support the mental work associated with the learning of written algorithms – with the resulting difficulties discussed above.

ALGORITHMS IN COMMON USE

At this stage in our analysis, it is helpful to have some more concrete examples to work with. This will prevent the discussion from straying too far from the particular and specific difficulties that actual teachers and children face. It will also help to curb the tendency towards over-generalisation which we find in some considerations of this topic. With this in mind, we will consider two mathematical topics: subtraction and division.

1. SUBTRACTION

Subtraction is usually introduced in the infant classroom as 'taking away', and is frequently not related to addition. However, it is very helpful if young children are encouraged to see the two processes as related. It is possible to read addition statements as requiring us to count further along the number line, and to read subtraction statements as requiring us either to count backwards along the line (i.e. the reverse of addition) or to count from one number to another (i.e. addition sums with 'holes' in: 6 + ❑ = 11). Mathematically speaking, the former is extremely useful in developing a mental model which could include subtracting a larger number from a smaller, and the latter supports the most useful mental strategies in establishing a difference and in working out change. The construction of 5 – 9 as 'start at five, and count nine steps backwards along the number line' is much more helpful, mathematically and pedagogically speaking, than its construction as 'five take away nine'. Also, connecting subtraction and addition (e.g. 24 – 6 = ❑ may be formulated as 6 + ❑ = 24) is of crucial importance in terms of later work in algebra, as well as being very useful in suggesting a counting-on strategy for performing the operation.

As children start performing the operation of subtraction, they can be encouraged to develop both a 'counting back' strategy and a 'counting on' strategy. Thus they may learn to count both forwards and backwards in tens. For example, 46 – 21 can be construed as 'forty-six, count backwards two tens – thirty-six, twenty-six – and count back one more to twenty-five'. They will also be developing mental strategies to count on, so that 45 – 29 can be read as 'How many from 29 to 45?' and performed as a 'count on one to thirty, then fifteen from thirty to forty-five' type of procedure. All of these mental procedures rely heavily upon two factors:

(i) The children need a mental image of a number line; an actual physical number line, which they can point to and count along, will be an essential stage in the development of this mental image.

(ii) The children need a good knowledge of the 'tens' – both the multiples of ten (as 'the next ten') and counting in tens.

Once the children reach Year 3 or Year 4, they are introduced to a written algorithm for dealing with subtractions such as 72 – 46. Previously, they may have been applying mental strategies to a written and vertical formulation, e.g.

$$\begin{array}{r} 68 \\ -35 \\ \hline \\ \hline \end{array}$$

where it was possible to take away or count back, dealing with tens or units first. At this juncture, when children need to move on to the next stage of difficulty, many are faced with the procedure known as decomposition or 'borrowing'.

The decomposition algorithm emphasises the place value aspects of our number system. For this reason, it was selected in preference to other methods at a time when teaching understanding was a paramount objective for teachers and a visual checking procedure was required by auditors in the workplace. However, it is worth remembering that there are, and have been, many voices raised in opposition to the general use of this approach. Partly for mathematical interest, and partly to emphasise the variety of alternatives, we will explore some different ways of carrying out a subtraction.

Many computer programmers prefer a nines complement algorithm, in which subtraction is replaced by addition. We start with 765 – 289. The computer replaces each digit of 765 with its nines complement. Thus the 7 becomes a 2, the 6 a 3 and the 5 a 4. The modified calculation becomes 234 + 289, which gives 523. The nines complement routine is applied again, transforming the 5 to a 4, the 2 to a 7 and the 3 to a 6. This gives the answer 476.

The idea of using a complements algorithm has been developed by several writers over the years. Caleb Gattegno in *The Common Sense of Teaching Mathematics* (1974) used a complements approach with a standard written layout which is efficient and not too difficult to follow:

765 – 289

Look at the second number. I want to raise it to the next hundred, so that I can subtract a multiple of 100 from 765. To do this I add a 1 to the 9 in 289 to create a 0. This gives me a 'carry' digit, turning the 8 tens into 9 tens. I now add a 1 to the 9 in the tens to create a 0 in this column. This also produces a carrying digit and makes the hundreds digit a 3. I have now reached the next hundred.

I can simplify this by adding the complement to the top number as I go, thus preserving the same difference between the two numbers.

765		766		776
–289	+ 1	290	+ 10	300
				476

I need to know that by keeping the difference between the two numbers the same, I can add to the number being subtracted and create a simpler calculation; and that that this transformation leaves the result unchanged. Gattegno's involvement in marketing Cuisinaire rods ties in clearly with this type of algorithm, since the rods offer an ideal model for demonstrating that a constant difference is preserved when adding equal amounts to two different numbers.

Another method, used by a school in North Oxfordshire, relies upon a knowledge of negative numbers.

	765	
	– 289	
subtract the hundreds	500	
subtract the tens	–20	(60 – 80 = –20)
subtract the units	–4	(5 – 9 = –4)
find the total	476	

A teacher in a school in Gosport announced to her Year 6 class that they had to start using the decomposition method in preference to their 'home-grown' algorithms since they were about to go to secondary school, and the teachers there would expect them to use decomposition. Anna, a child in the class, argued vigorously against this. She used 2165 – 1279 to demonstrate the superiority of 'her' method:

> Two thousand take one thousand leaves one thousand, so I write it down underneath as 1000. Next I do one hundred take away two hundred, that's minus one hundred, write it down underneath. Then sixty take away seventy, that's minus ten, write that down underneath. Last, five take away nine is minus four. Write that down. Now say a thousand minus a hundred leaves nine hundred. Nine hundred minus ten is eight hundred and ninety, minus another four is eight hundred and eighty-six. Write down the answer. You don't have to do all those crossings out like you did, Miss, you just do it!

2. DIVISION

Many children (and not a few adults) find division very difficult. All those numbers which seemed so familiar in addition, subtraction and multiplication now seem to behave very differently. One possible reasons for this is that the division sign undergoes a transformation in how it is read as children move from infant to junior level. In the infant school an expression such as 12 ÷ 3 is generally read as 'twelve shared between three'. However, by the time we come to Year 4, the same expression is read very differently as 'twelve divided by three' – or, departing even further from the infant model, as 'three into twelve goes...'. The notion of 'sharing' is, of course, abandoned in the juniors since it leads to no algorithm. In the infant classroom, the children share out the objects physically, a cumbersome and essentially non-mathematical process which involves counting out the total and then distributing the objects one at a time to each of the piles. The relationship between multiplication and division is not emphasised, and thus the multiplication facts are usually not brought into play.

The number line, which has been a very useful model for the other operations, appears a cumbersome way of representing division. Suddenly, it is not such a comfortable model.

0 1 2 3 4 5 6 7 8 9 10 11

10 ÷ 3 using the number line:

- jump back in threes;
- count the jumps;
- count the leftovers (if any).

It is not at all obvious what is happening, nor what strategy is required if the number line is to provide an effective model for the process of division. Internalising a technique like the one given above is certainly not easy in the absence of a helpful visual image.

It is here that a linguistic model can provide a great deal of support. Teachers provide not only the vocabulary with which to read the divisions, but also the interpretations in mathematical terms. Thus a confident child may 'read' 47 ÷ 6 as meaning:

> Forty-seven divided by six...
> won't go exactly...
> six goes into forty-seven so many times
> how many sixes in forty-seven?
> six divided into forty-seven
> forty-seven can be divided into six piles and there will be the same number in each pile and some left over...

It is clear that children's success in internalising a useful reading or interpretation of division is dependent upon a high level of fluency in (and comfort with) the other three operations, and especially a competence in multiplication. An ability to call up not only multiplication facts, but also addition and subtraction facts, at will is a necessary precursor for success in division. The traditional long and short division algorithms demand that you search for a particular multiple. For example, 671 ÷ 8 (after an initial scrutiny) requires a search for the multiple of eight which is closest to, but less than, 67. Thus a good starting point when teaching division is to prepare the ground by supplying lists of multiples. At the beginning, when it is essential that children focus on and get to grips with the actual procedure, it is helpful to have lists of multiples up on the wall or hanging from a line in a place in the classroom where everyone can see them (see Figure 2).

Figure 2

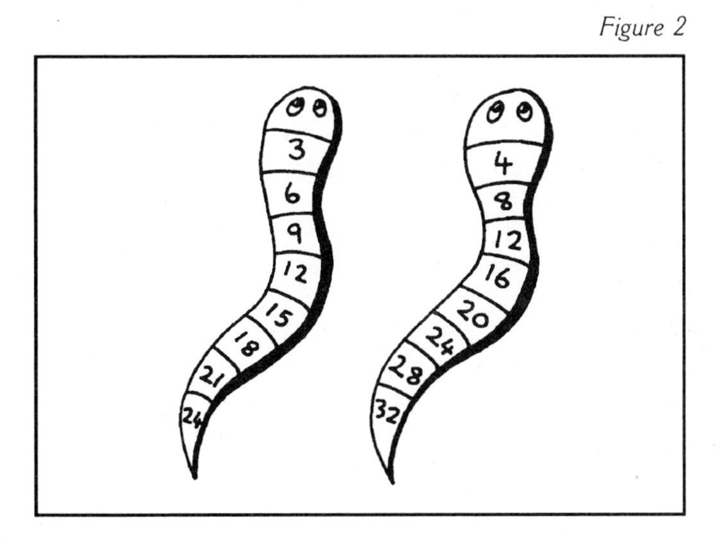

It is then much easier to perfect the standard 'long division' algorithm, since the child has only to focus upon the procedure and is not having to struggle to find the nearest multiple.

```
      8  3     r.7
   ________
8 | 6  7  1
    6  4
    ____
       3  1
       2  4
       ____
          7
```

However, as children progress, we can encourage them to devise those multiplication facts they are not sure of from those they remember. Thus a redesigned layout for the algorithm could be:

1 × 8	8	8 671
2 × 8	16 (double 8)	−240 30
		431
4 × 8	32 double to get next line	−240 30
		191
8 × 8	64	−160 20
		31
10 × 8	80 halve this to get next line	−16 2
5 × 8	40	15
20 × 8	160 (double 10 × 8)	−8 1
30 × 8	(10 × 8) + (20 × 8)	7

This algorithm, which uses a technique of repeated subtraction, allows children to use the multiples they are comfortable with, instead of making them guess at a division fact when they have no good memory of the corresponding multiplication fact. The list of multiples is derived by doubling, halving and multiplying by ten. The calculation starts by using the results of adding ten eights and twenty eights to get thirty eights. Subtracting 240 from the total still leaves 431 to be processed. Another 30 lots of 8 can then be subtracted, leaving 191, and the process continues until a remainder of less than 8 is left. Which multiples to use remains the child's choice. When the child's confidence is greater, the slowness of this repetitive method is likely to be self-corrected by the child or brought up by the teacher. Improving its efficiency is likely to be dependent upon greater familiarity, and also upon a better knowledge of multiples – which the teacher can work on in class.

Algorithms are social phenomena, the result of historical and social processes and events. Just a few miles from schools in England, across the Channel, children are taught a procedure similar to the one outlined above. To find the answer to 457 ÷ 7 using the French method, the computation is set out as follows:

457 ÷ 7	457	7
	37	
	2	65

Question: How many times does 7 go into 45?
Reply: Six, with remainder 3 because 7 x 6 = 42 and 3 more is 45.
Write the 6 and the remainder 3. Bring down the 7 and write it next to the 3 to make 37.
Question: How many 7s in 37?
Reply: Five, with remainder 2 because 5 x 7 = 35 and 2 more is 37.
Write down the 5 to the right of the 6 to produce 65.
Enter the 2 in the correct column under the 7.

As we have commented before, teachers are more inclined to insist upon one (and only one) algorithm for division, and are less likely to allow other procedures than they do for multiplication and subtraction. However, this uniformity does not seem to have resulted in confident dividers. Discussing with children how they read, and make sense of, the notion of division would seem to be a necessary precursor to a reappraisal of the algorithms currently applied in teaching division.

WHAT IS TO BE DONE?

Why do so many children have problems with algorithms? How can we improve upon the current situation, in which a substantial proportion of sixteen-year-olds appear to leave school without any numerical fluency?

The level of knowledge and skill required to perform most common written algorithms is not very great. The playing of many computer games demands the storage and processing of much more information, much more quickly, than is needed to perform most written algorithmic computations. Many children will continue to experience difficulties until:

- Their mental numerical skills are sufficiently well developed for them to perform basic mental computations, such as doubling and halving or adding, subtracting and multiplying by ten.
- They have acquired sufficient key number facts, such as the number bonds to ten and some key subtraction and multiplication facts.
- Teachers are aware of the errors which tend to become

incorporated into written algorithms, and can thus help children to recognise and correct these errors.

✧ Strategies are provided for self-checking or finding errors – at present, there is very little incentive to check pages of written sums, especially if the teacher is going to mark them all anyway.

✧ Mental methods are developed and reinforced with regular oral practice.

✧ Teachers are sensitive to possible difficulties arising through a conflict between mental and written strategies.

One feature of current classrooms which has received little direct attention in the press is the effect of a high degree of reliance upon commercially-produced workbooks and work cards. Heavy reliance on a text, or a series of pages to be completed, forces children to work individually, at the expense of small-group and whole-class discussion. Children tend to be working on different topics and different pages, which reduces to a minimum the opportunities for the teacher to lead the whole class in exposition, explanation, discussion or even the oral repetition of key skills. It is no exaggeration to say that, in such a system, teachers simply cannot make use of many of the techniques of teaching. This situation persists despite the encouragement of many writers to make classrooms places where children and teachers talk about maths and share ideas, and despite the fact that many teachers do just this in other subject areas.

Many classrooms also lack regular weekly lessons devoted to looking at children's acquired mental methods for calculating. This type of lesson is very different from those which test children's knowledge of tables, number bonds and speed of recall through individual pencil-and-paper arithmetic tests. By contrast, they are oral lessons, tackling a few problems in depth and discussing the strategies children can use for performing a mental calculation. The children themselves will offer strategies, and the teacher can demonstrate some of these. A key strategy offers a focus for the children who appear to need most assistance; this strategy can be modelled by the teacher, alongside the use of verbal or physical prompts. Thus a teacher might model how to multiply a two-digit number larger than 12 by a single-digit number, using a procedure which focuses on the tens digit first and then uses the prompt 'Hold it in your head' as the next part of the multiplication is performed. Thus '17 x 4' becomes '10 x 4 is 40, hold forty in my head [physically putting one finger on my head] and 7 x 4 is 28, so add on the 40 I'm holding, makes 68'.

In lessons of this kind, teachers select a computation which most children in the class can perform with confidence and accuracy, but which cannot be performed through instant recall. The choice has to be a subtle one, where children are likely to succeed but still have to work hard to produce a correct result. An important part of the lesson is the recounting by different children of their thinking as they perform the calculation. They literally 'talk us through' their working. The teacher praises diversity, creativity and ingenuity, and seeks to produce a classroom environment which is rich in possibilities and in which alternative methods are described confidently by children who have used them. At the same time, those children who need the security of a method provided by the teacher and reinforced by teacher demonstration are encouraged to practise it and develop confidence in its operation.

KEY SKILLS

Again and again, what emerges from these lessons is the need for familiarity with basic techniques. Children who are confident in their number work constantly draw upon these, and utilise a relatively small number of crucial strategies. It is worth noting that numerically confident children are not always those with the best memory, or the best instant recall of number facts. However, they *are* those who can access a number fact fast and effortlessly, using a technique such as doubling or halving, or drawing upon a resource such as their fingers. Those who are struggling to attain numerical fluency need to have these basic techniques constantly reinforced, and are also likely to be more dependent upon memorised algorithms. It is thus important, with these children, for number facts to be rehearsed, so that their recall becomes more automatic. It is a feature of all so-called 'basic' techniques that they belong to the realm of oral or mental maths, and so must be practised orally. Children need to talk! These key skills include:

- ✧ rounding up and down to a more convenient, or memorable, number;
- ✧ adjusting calculations in order to work with multiples of ten;
- ✧ doubling and halving;
- ✧ working with digits of larger value first;
- ✧ recall and use of learned number facts in creative ways, such as using fingers for a multiplication table.

For many children who lack confidence and facility with numbers, there is rapid improvement when it is openly acknowledged by the teacher and the other children that part of being good at numbers is being able to swap a nasty-looking sum for an easier equivalent that will give the same answer. Examples include changing 63 – 39 to 64 – 40, changing 14 x 9 to 14 x 10 take away 14, and changing 48 ÷ 8 into 48 halved three times. Knowing that you are *allowed* to change a sum into something 'easier' is all that many children need. An important part of this oral maths process is welcoming children's guesses and interim answers, even when they have made an error, and seeing any mistake as an opportunity for discussion and further elaboration of the problem. There is no room in this approach for ridicule or disparaging criticism. Children have to be allowed to experiment, knowing not only that the teacher will help them if they stray off track, but also that they will not suffer embarrassment or ridicule as a consequence.

CONCLUSIONS

There is little doubt that many children, and not a few adults, have insufficient facility for performing algorithms, particularly in complex mental calculations. Perhaps more sadly, many children and adults have never acquired a 'feel' for number, a comfortableness and fluency when working with numbers. Indeed, numbers are more commonly a source of fear than of joy or interest. The reasons for this mathematical malaise are likely to be complex and various, and will resist simple answers or easy solutions. However, in this chapter we have attempted to categorise and describe some of the more commonly observed problems, to speculate as to their causes, and finally to suggest ways of teaching and a curriculum content which might improve things.

The problems we have discussed fall basically into two types. Firstly, there are those which arise when children cannot complete a procedure, and are either unable to remember what to do next or are so immersed in the difficulties of the arithmetic needed that they have lost track of where they have got to in the procedure itself. The provision of a set of resources upon which children can draw is of immense value here. These resources could include:

✧ number facts (e.g. lists of multiples, visual depictions of number bonds);

✧ mathematical aids, such as number lines or grids, coins or cubes;

✧ cognitive strategies, such as 'counting on' and rounding up or down;

✧ verbal prompts, such as 'carry the ten' or 'bring down the next digit' (in long division).

Secondly, there are those difficulties which occur through a conflict between two alternative and possibly incompatible procedures. Most commonly, these are seen when the child has a mental algorithm which involves the use of a strategy that runs counter to the technique required to complete the written algorithm successfully. Conflicts between algorithms also arise when children have learned or invented an algorithm which is different from that being taught by the teacher. Teachers need to be aware of, and sensitive to, both types of difficulty mentioned here.

It is clear that methods of teaching can make a great deal of difference to children's numeracy. This chapter has placed emphasis on the following pedagogical strategies:

✧ Direct teaching, incorporating exposition, explanation and the frequent demonstration of numerical strategies and techniques.

✧ The provision of frequent, regular and relaxed opportunities for the children to articulate their mathematical thinking, to talk about their ways of getting an answer and to work through their methods and strategies verbally with each other and with their teacher. It must not be better to 'shut up than be shown up'!

✧ Encouraging a certain amount of oral repetition – little and often, rather than in indigestible chunks. This particularly applies to techniques such as counting in tens, rounding up or down, finding the next ten, doubling and halving, and other key skills. It does not only apply to multiplication facts and number bonds, though these are included.

✧ Continuously monitoring the children's mental methods and skills, their factual knowledge of tables and number bonds, their strategies of estimation and approximation. This monitoring needs to occur in whole-class situations (with the teacher posing a problem and inviting children to use their own methods of solving it), and also in small groups and with individual children.

Throughout this chapter, we have stressed the need for many different kinds of *talk*: discussion on the part of teachers and pupils; articulation of procedures and strategies; the questions and answers of a productive dialogue with the teacher, with friends and with oneself. Not for nothing do we speak of numerical *fluency* – the effective mathematical classroom is certainly not silent!

CHAPTER 6

BILINGUAL CHILDREN LEARNING NUMBER

This chapter is about bilingual children becoming numerate and having full access to their relevant national curriculum for mathematics. It explores some of the things a teacher needs to consider when providing for the mathematical learning needs of bilingual children. In writing this chapter, I am drawing on my experience of teaching in primary schools and of working in two other countries: Bangladesh and the Lao People's Democratic Republic (Laos).

In Britain, there are many young children who regularly speak one or more languages other than English. (It is worth noting that more than half the world's population use more than one language in their everyday lives.) The term *bilingual*, in this chapter, refers to children who use two (or more) languages in their home and school lives; they may be children who are at the beginning of learning to speak English, or children who switch competently between one or more home/ community languages and English. It is important to recognise that, as they move between languages, the children move between cultures with all the flexibility and skill that demands (Skutnabb-Kangas and Cummins, 1988) and that as bilingual children in English schools are usually from ethnic minority families, many are aware of the diversity that exists within a society and of the discrimination and prejudice that can result from being 'different'.

TALKING MATHEMATICS

When working with children who are beginners in English, the first question a teacher must ask is 'How can I ensure that we understand each other?' To explore this question I quote, below, a section of a conversation I recorded when Shahida, who was then aged five years nine months, was working with her two friends Shazia (aged five years six months) and Shopna (aged five years four months). All three are Punjabi/Urdu speakers, all in the stage of learning English. The task was to measure the height of one of the group, using large plastic bricks. As they worked, Shahida and her friends talked all the time in their shared language. A monolingual teacher joined the group when two towers had been built to the same height as Shopna: one with thick bricks, the other with thin ones. The conversation went like this:

1 Teacher: How many of the thick bricks did you use in this one? *(The teacher's hand indicates the tower she is talking about.)*

2 Shazia: Twelve, Miss. *(She indicates the written record they have made.)*

3 Shahida: No, Miss. Not just, Miss. Not same. This bit too much. *(With her fingers above Shopna's head, she shows by how much the brick is higher.)*

4 Teacher: Oh, you couldn't make it exactly the same size. You had some left over. You could say it was 11 and a bit bricks, then – 11 bricks and this much. *(The teacher indicates with her fingers. Shahida swaps the top brick for a thinner one.)*

5 Shahida: See, Miss.

6 Teacher: OK, 11 thick bricks and one thin one. What about the thinner ones? *(indicating the other tower).* How many of these ones did you need? *(The children consult their paper again.)*

7 *(The children talk in Punjabi.)*

8 Shazia: 23, Miss, 23.

9 Teacher: So you used 23 thin ones?

10 Shopna: Yes, Miss, 23 Miss.

11 Shahida: Big bricks don't need more. Little bricks bigger. Look...

12 Shazia: Miss, little bricks er... er... *(She looks at Shahida and speaks in Punjabi.)*

13 Shahida: More. Look, Miss – two little bricks same, same big one. *(putting together two thin bricks to show they are the same as one big brick).*

14 Teacher: So you need twice as many little bricks as big bricks.

15 Shopna: *(Building two wide bricks and four narrow bricks)*

Yes. See, Miss, see.

16 Teacher: OK, three thick bricks *(taking three bricks)*. How many thin ones? *(Shopna takes thin bricks and starts to build.)*

17 Shahida: Six, Miss.

18 Shazia: Six, Miss.

19 Teacher: Four bricks.

20 Shahida: Eight.

21 Teacher: OK, what have you have found out? Two big bricks are the same height as four little bricks. OK, how many big bricks will you need to measure Shazia? *(Shopna starts to build another tower next to Shazia.)* Just a minute. Before you do that, can you think how many you are going to need?

22 *(Conversation in Punjabi; Shahida leading the conversation.)*

23 Teacher: Is Shazia taller or shorter than Shopna?

24 Shahida: I know, Miss: Shazia, bigger. (*She pushes Shazia next to the tower to show that she is the same height as the tower.)*

25 Teacher: Yes, how many then, Shopna?

26 Shopna: Oh, same, 12.

27 Teacher: How can we write all this down to tell the others? *(She brings out paper and pens.)*

Shahida and her friends are beginners in English, but not beginners in communication. The teacher was able to use the English language, supported by gestures, to focus the children's attention on significant aspects of the activity (point 21) and to offer challenges to the children's thinking (21). Clemson and Clemson (1994) argue that 'mathematics must involve activity, thinking and talk'. The above passage shows the children and their teacher moving between activity, thinking and talking in two languages, and how the processes interact to develop the children's thinking. The children switch between languages (7) and (22); and at one point (12), Shazia apparently asks Shahida to help her with an English word.

Beginners in English are not without language, and their linguistic abilities should be used positively in school. At the beginning of the primary years of schooling, children have a competent and growing command of the uses of language.

A communicative inventory of five-year-olds' attainment by Maggie MacLure, drawing on the work of the National Oracy Project (K. Norman ed., 1992), shows that children at the age of five have (among many other attainments) a vocabulary of several thousand words, the ability to use talk to further their own learning and the ability to disconnect talk from the immediate context – the language skills they need for their mathematics learning. Perhaps more stunningly, research suggests that during the primary years children add nine new words a day to their vocabulary! These skills are not specific to the English language. Children all over the world learn languages in very different contexts (Heath, 1983; Tizard and Hughes, 1984) – but we can be confident that by the time they come to school they can use language in many ways, including as a problem-solving tool.

A teacher needs evidence to assess children's attainment. From the discussion quoted above, the teacher could record the children's understanding that large measures tally fewer units than smaller ones used to measure the same object; that measures are not exact; that you can use what you have already found out to predict the answers to further questions, and so on. She could also see the differences between the children's attainments. Shahida (points 16–20) was enjoying playing with the relationships between numbers in her head, while Shopna needed to model the problem with bricks.

The children were not yet able to express in English ideas such as '11 and a bit bricks tall' (point 4); yet in other ways, the conversation is remarkably similar to the sample given by SCAA (1995) as a example of the mathematical language typical of Level 2:

> Child: This row is big bear, little bear. It doesn't matter what colour they are – big, little, big, little!
>
> Teacher: What about this row?
>
> Child: Big, smaller and smallest, and they're yellow, red, yellow, red.
>
> Teacher: What about this line?
>
> Child: Well, there's a big one, smaller one and smallest bear, but the pattern is green, yellow, red, blue, green, yellow, red, blue.

In both cases the children are expressing ideas, responding to the teacher's questioning and expressing comparisons. Shahida (point 3) says, 'Not same. This bit too much' and (24) 'Shazia bigger'. The Punjabi-speaking children are using two languages; they are able to move between them and use understandings in one language to support them in another. At (22), it seems Shazia and Shopna may not have understood and are using Punjabi to clarify the meaning. The languages are interdependent; both are available as a learning resource.

THE CONTEXT OF MATHEMATICS

The way we structure mathematics learning in our classrooms offers a view of what mathematics is. It also shows the children how they should go about learning it. Somboon, a six-year-old boy living in Laos, was asked what he liked about school. He answered, 'I want to go to school to learn. I want to learn letters and numbers. I want to read and do sums.' The demands on him were narrower than those on a child of a similar age in England, and many Lao children were not successful in the system; but his school and family were united in a clear idea of what school was and what he had to do to succeed. Part of Shahida's and her friends' success was that they were offered clear expectations and that they were used to taking part in such dialogue and seeing their friends work in this way. They knew that their contribution was valued and that their attempts in English were taken seriously.

Clemson and Clemson (1994) quote the psychologist Ausubel's three factors which motivate children to undertake a task:

- interest in the task;
- the effect the task has on our image of ourselves;
- whether the task affords us links to what we already know.

Children's attitudes are developed and built up over a long time, both at home and at school. The school attempts to create a climate which motivates children towards learning. For this to happen, the children have to feel that they are people who can succeed in mathematics. They need to attend a school which says to them, 'We welcome you as you are; we respect your particular experience as a good basis of learning; we value you because of who you are, not in spite of who you are.' The development of such an ethos is important, and not only to bilingual children. Mathematics learning challenges all children's thinking; they need to be supported through that challenge by teachers who believe in their ability to succeed.

For many years, mathematics was seen as a self-standing subject: one in which the internal relationships are all-important, with the child's role being only to learn and manipulate those relationships. However, we have come to realise that mathematics can no longer be considered, learned and taught in a kind of splendid isolation, untainted by cultural life. Mathematics is a socio-historical construct, and is learned by children who live in particular cultural and ethnic contexts. Unfortunately, we live in a society in which many children from ethnic minority backgrounds will have been subject to the undermining effects of prejudice and overt racism. Moreover, self-esteem has long been correlated with high academic performance (see, for example, Purkey, 1970).

Gillian Pugh (in the foreword to Siraj-Blatchford, 1994) says this:

> Children begin to form attitudes towards themselves and others from what they see and hear around them – from their families and their friends, from books and the media. For many children this learning includes racial attitudes, and we know that many children as young as three or four are beginning to feel discriminated against.

The building of children's self-esteem in relation to learning is the responsibility of the school. An important aspect of this is to demonstrate that the diversity of experience children bring to school is valued as a mathematics learning resource.

The National Curriculum for England and Wales acknowledges the relationship between mathematics learning and socio-cultural identity for Welsh children:

> In Wales, pupils should be given opportunities, where appropriate, in their study of mathematics, to develop and apply their

> knowledge and understanding of the cultural, economic, environmental, historical and linguistic characteristics of Wales.

This passage validates the view that mathematics can be a vehicle for the promotion of cultural identity.

NUMBERS FROM AROUND THE WORLD

Going into classrooms nowadays, the visitor often has a strong sense that the children in these classes come from a variety of cultural and linguistic backgrounds. There are often representations of children's home languages and maps which show the places of origin of the children's families: artefacts, materials and artwork from many parts of the world.

In this section, I will argue that not only does the acknowledgement of a child's background support her or his identity as a learner, but, also that there are useful gains in mathematics learning to be made from such an approach. These points are illustrated by the example of some work which took place in a Year 2 class, concerned with developing the children's understanding of place value (see the England and Wales National Curriculum for Mathematics at Key Stage 1, Programme of Study for Number, Section 2b: 'read, write and order numbers... depending on an understanding that the position of a digit signifies its value.')

The school had identified a need to involve families more directly in the mathematics curriculum. Closer contact would offer opportunities to exchange views of what mathematics teaching and learning should be and to explain school policies. It was decided to collect number systems from around the world, using the expertise of parents and families as a resource. Parents and other family members wrote the number systems they knew on number lines from 1–10 and recorded them on cassettes. Parents wrote Chinese, Arabic, Hebrew, Bengali, Gujerati, Hindi, Roman and Urdu numerals using symbol systems different from the system we normally use (which is historically derived from Hindu and Arabic numerals). They spoke Russian, French, Italian, German, Welsh, Gaelic and Irish into the cassette recorder. One immediate gain was an enthusiasm for numbers!

Numbers became a normal topic of conversation in the classrooms and between parents and teachers.

A range of activities was developed, at a number of levels. The children were all involved in comparing, ordering and counting activities, from simple matching games to elaborate sorting and counting routines. As the mathematical gains became apparent, parents were asked to supply numbers to a hundred. One Year 2 class undertook a number of activities with 100 squares in different symbol systems. Counting in twos, three, fives and tens, the children looked at the patterns that were made. They compared and contrasted the systems, and naturally questions arose. Two boys were talking intently in Sylheti, comparing Bengali, Chinese and English numbers. 'Miss, Miss,' they told their teacher, 'number 10. Bengali, look two numbers. English, look two numbers, Chinese one number'. They had noticed that in many, but not all, number systems the number ten is written with two characters. The teacher was able to build on this insight and lead them to an understanding of the way the system of Hindu/Arabic numbers is constructed. By seeing that our way of writing numbers is one of a number of possible systems, and by understanding that it was created by people for people's convenience, they were able to make place value less mysterious.

Of course, not all children make the same leaps of understanding as these two boys did; but insights gained were shared with the rest of the class, and so became common currency in the classroom. The work was supported by other activities and exercises on place value, and many children – both monolingual and bilingual – could confidently demonstrate the understanding that 'the position of a digit signifies its value' and could use their knowledge of pattern and regularity to write numbers to 1 000.

MATHEMATICAL LANGUAGE AND LANGUAGE IN MATHEMATICS LEARNING

It is probably no longer necessary, as it was ten years ago, to make a case for language being important to mathematics learning. Children's ability to *talk* mathematics is stressed in, for example, the National Curriculum for England and Wales. They are required to express ideas in a precise way, and to use technical language. Shahida, whose measuring work is discussed above, could not yet articulate ideas precisely in English, but she had begun to play a full part in mathematical dialogue.

There is much well-documented research (see especially *Thinking Voices: the Work of the National Oracy Project* (K. Norman, ed., 1992) to show that beginners in English can increase their attainment, not least in mathematics, by learning through their home language with a teacher who speaks the same language. However, there are far too few teachers who are speakers of the home and community languages of their pupils, and a class may contain children from 15 or more language backgrounds. As staffing is squeezed because of cuts, monolingual teachers have less and less access to bilingual support.

Nonetheless, teachers can create procedures which welcome children's use of their home/community languages; these can be incorporated into the structure of curriculum planning, with benefit to all involved. Older children can find it a valuable experience to work with younger children and revisit their early learning; parents and community members can benefit from seeing how mathematics learning is planned and executed in a classroom. Bilingual children can explore mathematical ideas in their most familiar language; and by demonstrating that minority languages are suitable vehicles for learning mathematics, all children gain greater respect for them.

Mathematical English is a 'new' language for all children. Since it is specifically a classroom language, it will be learned mostly in school. The difficulties all children face when presented with this new language have been noted in a number of accounts (see especially Pimm, 1987).

Maths Talk, a Mathematical Association publication (1992), shows that all children have to learn that words in mathematics are often used differently from the way they are used in everyday life – for example, 'take away', 'volume' and 'face'. Children have to understand that, even within mathematics talk, words can have more than one meaning – for example, 'base' and 'square'. To become fluent in this new language, children must hear mathematics spoken in ways understandable to them and be included in mathematical dialogue at an early stage. Only then will they have relevant experiences to incorporate into their own speech.

For all of us, there is a great difference between speaking and understanding: between the language a person knows and that which he or she can produce on a given occasion. If you are learning or have learned a foreign language, think about the complexity of the structures you can hear and understand – then think about what happens when you try to reply! The teacher working with Shahida, Shazia and Shopna feels confident that the children will understand 'So you need twice as many little bricks as big bricks' (point 4), though she knows it will be some time before the children use this form.

Maths Talk argues that 'Barriers are often created between teacher and children by the premature use of technically correct language'. So when the teacher talks to Shahida and her friends, she is careful to monitor understanding, uses visual supports and rephrases (point 6) when she is not understood. Children must feel comfortable about displaying a lack of understanding, without losing self-esteem. If they are confident about experimenting with the language of maths, children are able to reflect on it in a sophisticated way. The story of Nobin illustrates this. We were talking about coconuts. 'What's on the outside of a coconut?' I asked. He looked puzzled. 'Outside, outside.' I picked a wooden shape and demonstrated what I meant by 'outside'. Later Nobin told me, 'I thinked outside was in the playground.'

Children will not produce technical language until they have had the time and experience to adopt it comfortably into their speech. The first step is to take part in mathematical discourse. During my time in school I have collected many examples of children going to great lengths to communicate mathematical ideas. One child in particular, Shahed, found a number of ways to express comparatives before he took on the standard English forms. He used language from a favourite story to compare three things: 'Look Miss, Father Bear, Mother Bear, Baby Bear.' Later he used 'Big, little big, little little'. To express comparison of weights he used 'Big heavy, little heavy, nothing heavy'; and for numbers, he said 'This one got lot, this one got some lot, this one got none lot'.

To allow these exchanges, the teacher must create an encouraging and receptive classroom. The children need to know that they are valued members of the group and that their contributions will be taken into account.

WORKING WITH CHILDREN LEARNING MATHEMATICS IN A SECOND LANGUAGE

In this section, I consider some things that support bilingual children's learning. The first thing I find out is exactly which languages a child speaks at home. Many parents tell the school that they speak 'Indian' or 'African', probably because they do not expect the school to recognise languages such as Yoruba or Twi. Other parents may give the national language of their country of origin, such as Urdu or Hindi, perhaps because it has higher status than their local language or dialect. It is worth persevering and finding out exactly, because recognising a child's language is very close to recognising her or his identity. And practically it is important when you are finding other speakers of the same language.

For children newly arrived in this country, it is valuable to find out the child's previous experience of schooling. Juhel, a five-year-old, had just arrived from Bangladesh and was admitted into the reception class. Even allowing for the adjustments Juhel and his family were having to make after moving from a rural community in Sylhet to inner-city London, Juhel was not settling well. He did not persist in any activity, he seemed unwilling to co-operate or work with others, and he spent a lot of the time moving from one thing to another and generally being a nuisance to others in the class. Through an older cousin, we were able to talk to him and find out that we did not match his expectation of a school. Juhel, in his Bangladeshi school, had been doing well and had just been allowed to do addition sums. He had been able to see his own progress and felt good about it. Moreover, his parents, unfamiliar with education in U.K. schools, talked disparagingly about what he was doing and were pressuring him 'to work, not play all day'. I have seen, in Bangladeshi villages, children taking a whitened board to school in the morning. The board is taken home at night to be re-whitened for the next day. On it is the child's work for the day, and the parents can see exactly what their child has done. Our system was not offering either parents or children that support. The school learned a lesson: not that we should try to reproduce a village school in Bangladesh, but that we should value that experience and understand the importance of it to Juhel and his family, and try to be more explicit about what we were teaching and why.

Reviewing materials is important. Much has been written about the powerful stereotypes that can be promoted through the materials children use. Mathematical materials can give powerful messages about who does mathematics and, by omission, who doesn't. Children can themselves take on the process of evaluating text books or workbooks. Records of the numbers of boys and girls depicted, the races and nationalities represented, the roles each play and so on can be kept on a database and offer opportunities for data handling activities.

Review the content of your mathematics programme as well. Within the framework of the relevant national curriculum, decisions have to be made about how and in what context the content should be taught. The Runnymede Trust (1993) has published a book which shows that the content of the curriculum in each subject area can reflect a diversity of backgrounds while fulfilling the curriculum requirements.

Talk with (and listen to) parents, and wherever possible involve them in the children's learning. For some parents, it is necessary to find a translator – start with your own staff, making sure you know all the languages represented. Older children and other parents can help; but if the issues are confidential, it may be necessary to find an outsider you both have confidence in. Community and neighbourhood groups may be able to suggest translators; local doctors, libraries and places of worship can be good sources of information.

Some parents, like Juhel's, may find it difficult to voice unease at what they see happening in the classroom. They may have legitimate worries which need to be addressed. Parents may themselves have had poor experiences of schooling, or may have been educated in very different systems and find it difficult to understand the school's approaches. In these circumstances, the school needs to be explicit about mathematical objectives. Parents often feel reassured when the mathematical content of the programme is made explicit, and they understand that it has been carefully prepared and structured.

The curriculum should be designed to reflect the chronological and mental ages of children, rather than their ability in English. The measuring task described in this chapter was suitable for five- and six-year-old children; a ten-year-old child with an equivalent level of English would need a task at a ten-year-old level. Tasks which are too easy or babyish lower the child's self-esteem and her or his status in the eyes of the rest of the class.

This approach has benefits for monolingual children. It has been argued that speakers of more than one language may have an advantage which can particularly assist mathematics learning. Bilingual children may be more able to generalise and think in abstractions from an early age. In classrooms where multilingualism is valued, monolingual children see languages other than English in regular use and discover that ideas can be expressed with more than one set of symbols. In these circumstances, monolingual children may well learn at an earlier age to stand outside their own thinking and to reflect upon it. The potential advantages can only be realised in settings that genuinely welcome diversity and use it as a positive resource. Monolingual children who see the languages and cultures of others given value and status are helped to address some of the negative attitudes and images to which they may have been exposed.

CONCLUSIONS

I have tried to make a number of points in this chapter.

Firstly, mathematics is a talking subject, and talk is as necessary to bilingual children as to those learning in their first language. Bilingual children are competent language users, and it is up to the monolingual teacher to devise strategies by which they can be involved in mathematical dialogue. Involvement in dialogue is needed both to support learning and to help children towards control of the technical language that they will need for future mathematics learning and communication. We cannot afford to wait until the children have more English before we teach mathematics: they need to learn mathematics now; and by doing mathematics, they will learn the English they need to know. For example, by taking part in the collection of data and interrogating the database created, children exercise relevant language as well as mathematical skills.

National curricula provide structures of required mathematical attainments; but learning and teaching methodologies are not yet prescribed, and the documentation is couched in terms which encourage practical work, discussion, exploration and investigation. The teacher needs to select materials and methodologies that will make access to the relevant curriculum a reality for bilingual children. Successful mathematics teaching includes supporting children's confidence and self-esteem as mathematics learners. Children in ethnic minority families may be subject to the pressures of prejudice and racism, which can have a negative effect on children's attainment. Support for self-esteem involves the acknowledgement of a children's ethnic and cultural identity. Making positive use in maths teaching of the child's linguistic and cultural experience will benefit her or his mathematical performance both directly (through making use of the opportunities for comparison and reflection that using more than one notation and measurement system provides) and indirectly (by indicating the value of systems from many different parts of the world).

Many of the things I have suggested here represent good practice for all children. Bilingual children need and deserve the best mathematical teaching practice; and I would agree with Wendy Suschitzky, who says in *Beginning Teaching, Beginning Learning* that 'giving every child entitlement to quality education is *just good practice*'.

CHAPTER 7

PLAY AND NUMBER

This chapter is an eclectic gathering of ideas. Some, I think, can be used directly with children; others are concerned more with theoretical issues related to teaching. I've given each collection of ideas its own sub-heading, to help organise the chapter into more manageable sections.

At the outset, I need to say something about play. My own view can be clearly stated. Without play, without access to play, the individual is not wholly well. Play nurtures wholeness and invites integration of experience into a developing sense. Here, I am not referring exclusively to children, but also to adults. In the 'overlap space' which adult and child both occupy in the teaching situation, it is essential that both engage in healthy play together. I do not mean to imply a separation of work from play. Healthy work – that is, work which is seen by the participant as enjoyable, purposeful, creative and rewarding – contains the essential ingredient of play: the facility for becoming absorbed, for losing oneself in the activity. Unhealthy work tends to lack this quality of 'involvement': it splits off intellectual activity from the individuals, imposing an alien framework of demands.

Playing with numbers is both work (certainly hard, at times intensely so) *and* an experience which does not demand or force a split-off intellect. The teacher's task, as I see it, is to be creatively involved in maintaining the overlap space between teacher and child within which are played out the social, interpersonal, cognitive and intellectual activities which we call teaching and learning. In short, it is the teacher's responsibility to maintain a context in which play is possible for both herself and the child.

DISCOVERING A NUMBER SEQUENCE

Young children need to develop an understanding of the structure of the number system alongside their growing ability to count sets of objects with increasing accuracy and efficiency. For some time, there has been an emphasis on cardinal counting in the early years over and above work on ordinal counting. Anxiety about working on the number system per se with children in the early years seems to emerge from the use of Piagetian frameworks for viewing children's activities. These frameworks can give rise to the notion that the manipulation of physical objects is an essential ingredient for all learning in mathematics. Work on ordinal counting is resisted by some teachers, who argue that it is too abstract and therefore conceptually too difficult for children.

However, young children can invent symbols to represent amounts (see Chapter 2, page 32). The unprompted exploration of visual images also seems part of children's natural curiosity. Some children as young as six have been reported as developing visual images of numbers for their own use.[1]

Children can explore ordinal counting by using numbered carpet squares placed in sequence. They can physically experience the movement needed to travel from 1 to 2 to 3 and from 7 to 6 to 5. They can sense the reversal needed to move first from 2 to 5 and then back to 2. As their experience increases and the line is extended, they can view the line while standing on 5 and see that 9 is further away than 7. (See Figure 1.)

The numbers 1 to 9, written on carpet squares, can be rearranged in a circular pattern with a tenth square blank. (See Figure 2.) A group of nine children can develop the work. Each of the following activities need take up only a few minutes on any one occasion. The

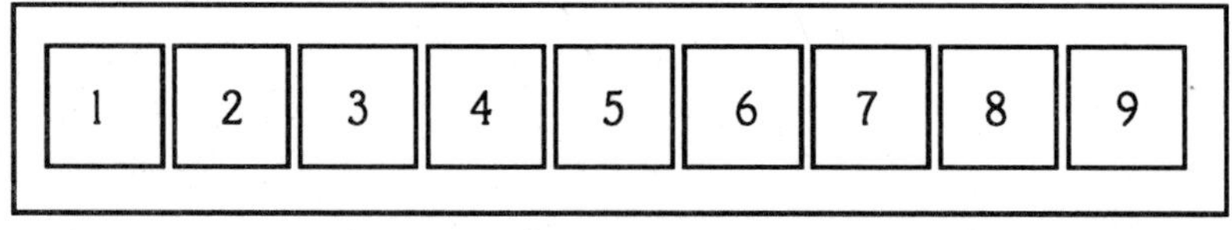

Figure 1

children sit in a circle facing inwards, with their carpet squares in front of them as an aide-mémoire. They do not have to read or name each other's numbers, so this arrangement of carpet squares shouldn't pose reading problems for the group. It may even be useful for the children to close their eyes during an activity – opening them only to check on their number, should they forget. The teacher takes the tenth place

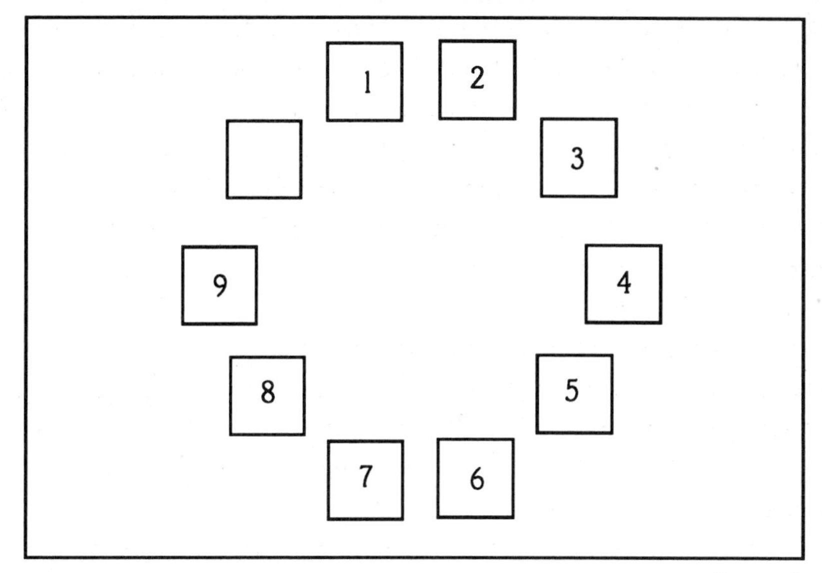

Figure 2

between 9 and 1 to make the 'decade' numbers.

In one activity, the teacher walks round the group in sequence, touching child 1, child 2 and so on. The children are prompted to say their numbers when touched. The activity can be developed later by child 1 saying her or his number and then touching child 2. Later still, the children may link hands; they call their number when they feel a hand being squeezed, then pass on the squeeze with their other hand to the next child in the circle.

Throughout, each child is responsible for saying only one number. They work together to build up the sequence from 1 to 9. They may start from numbers other than 1, working both forwards and backwards. What is being built up needs to be listened to by the group, and the teacher should draw the children's attention to the nature of the performance as a whole. Because they are not expected to remember the entire sequence, this activity is appropriate for children who cannot yet recite the number names in sequence (provided they can accept the social setting and operate within the rules of play).

What happens, of course, is that children begin to *hear* the recitation of the various sequences as a whole. Initially, the children's attention may be almost exclusively focused on maintaining their own performance.[2] As they become more comfortable with their individual role, they are increasingly able to place their attention on the group performance. They may then become able to say what a listener outside the group might hear.

By playing an active role in the 'decade' position, the teacher can introduce other variations as the children grow in confidence and fluency. 'I'm going to say some silly words and I want you to copy me. I'm going to say "sausages". (To child 1) You need to say "sausages-one". (To child 2) You need to say "sausages-two". (To child 3) I expect you know what to say!'... (This is then followed by the recitation.)

'This time I'll say another word, and (indicating child 1) you carry on. Forty.' If this count is successful, the teacher can continue by saying 'fifty' after 'forty-nine' is uttered by child 9.

The numbers which the children hear follow a 'rule' generated by the group. Sequences such as *thirty-eight, thirty-nine, thirty-ten, thirty-eleven*, which are often generated by children exploring the number system, do not emerge when the teacher operates in the decade position in this fashion. The teacher takes the children over the difficult parts of the count.

After involving children in a counting sequence involving several rounds, the teacher can ask which numbers 'belong' to which children. Not only might someone be able to recall that he or she has had to say six, forty-six and fifty-six, but observant children may well be able to report what they have noticed about other children's contributions. They are beginning to absorb information about the structure of the counting system from direct observation.

More complex work can include an exploration of the count through the use of rhythm. By alternately whispering and shouting (or crouching and jumping) as they recite the numbers in sequence, the children can generate patterns of even and odd numbers.

These activities involve becoming familiar with the structure of the number system. They are concerned with learning how to ask questions about *what comes next*, rather than about *how many in a set*. They provide a meaningful context for work on ordinal counting; they are intended to run alongside work on cardinal counting, not to be a substitute for it.

FINGERS AND BEADS

Recent work with a group of Malaysian teachers led to an interesting exchange of stories about their methods of teaching number. (See Figure 3.) From the age of seven, children are taught a finger method of counting which allows the representation of all numbers from 1 to 99. The fingers of the right hand are used to count from 1 to 4. The right thumb represents 5; when combined with the fingers, this allows the count to extend to 9 (thumb and first finger is 6, and so on). The fingers of the left hand represent 10 to 40, the left thumb 50; when combined with the left thumb, the fingers can then be used to represent 60 to 90.

The children use their hands to represent numbers, and then to represent calculations. This work takes place over a period of two years, at which point pupils are formally introduced to the use of the abacus. The type of abacus used has four beads below a central bar and one bead above, as shown in Figure 4. Consequently, its structure requires it to be used in a manner which resembles the hand counting process.

What does this experience make accessible to Malaysian children? There is a strong possibility that after a while, they will develop a visual memory which links specific finger *positions* with the associated numbers. Further, a kinaesthetic memory may develop such that specific finger *movements* are linked to calculations. In much the same way that a guitarist reads a chord sequence and uses a kinaesthetic memory of where the fingers must move to play the sequence, so the reading of a calculation may lead to 'automatic' finger movement and hence to the answer. The pupils need to learn a number of groupings of movements in relation to certain additions and subtractions. For example, in order to subtract 8, it is sometimes necessary to subtract a 10 and add two ones, while other subtractions of 8 require a subtraction of a 5 followed by three ones.

The decision about which routine to use depends on an ability to 'read' the hand arrangement, and subsequently the abacus pattern. The abacus is read from right to left. The user 'reads' the beads that are placed against the central bar. (See Figure 4.)

The process of using the abacus seems to lead to a strong

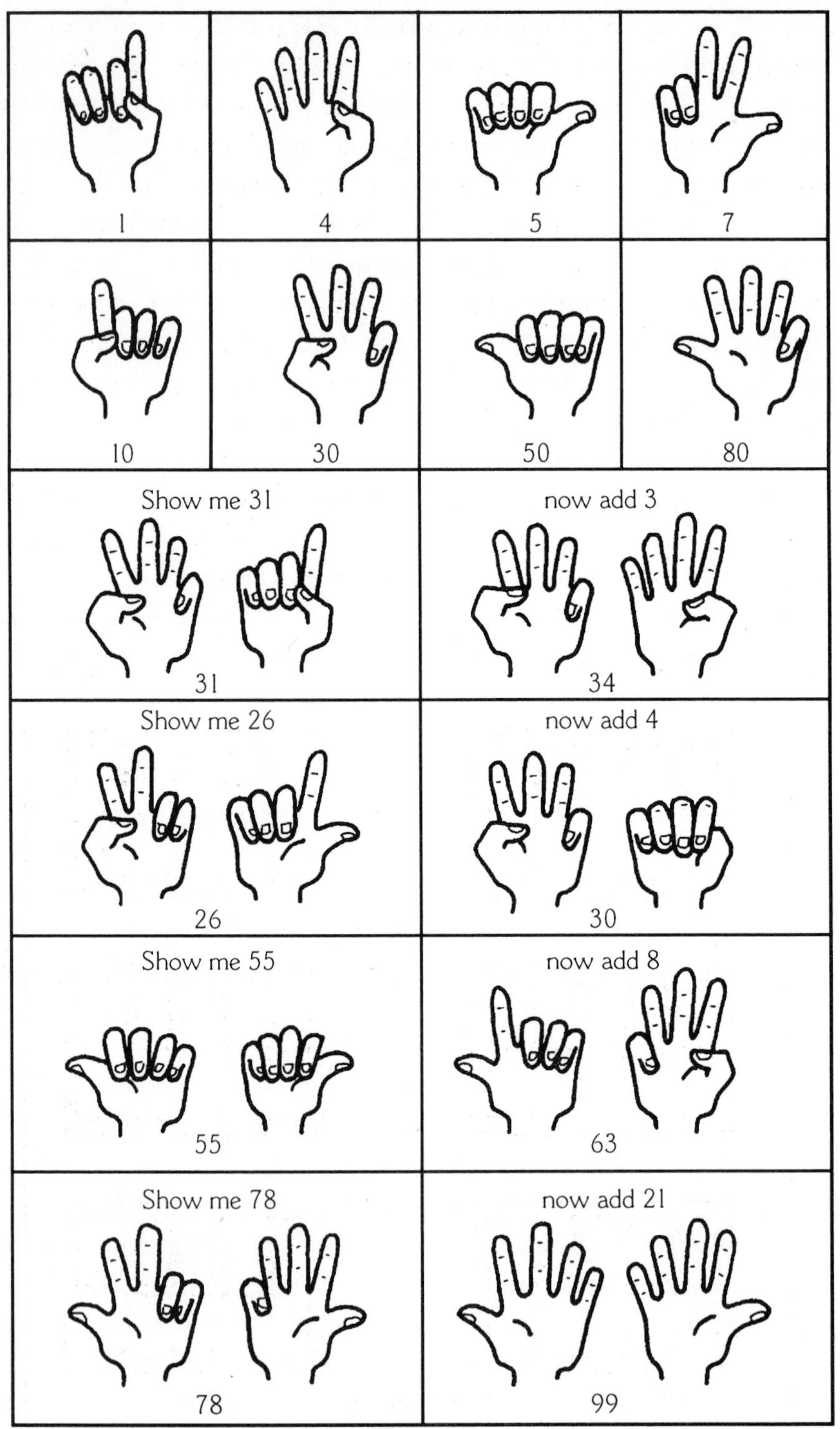
1
4
5
7
10
30
50
80
Show me 31
31
now add 3
34
Show me 26
26
now add 4
30
Show me 55
55
now add 8
63
Show me 78
78
now add 21
99

Figure 3

association between factual knowledge, facility with algorithms for computation, and the development of a visual and kinaesthetic memory of bead movements (the development of which parallels that of the finger movements learned earlier). Where such strong associations exist, learners have access to what they know via an increased range of routes. Memory of visual and kinaesthetic sequences can strongly support the associated cognitive processes.[3] Hand and bead positions represent numbers, and the movements represent calculations. The activities can be said to act as *metaphors* for the number situations they represent. In this way, they are not unlike Cuisenaire rods or Dienes arithmetic blocks.

The Malaysian teachers model the hand movements for their children. The children need to internalise the intermediate steps to performing each calculation. Later, the teachers use chalkboards to write sequences of calculations for their pupils to perform.

As an example of how calculations can be broken down by this

Figure 4

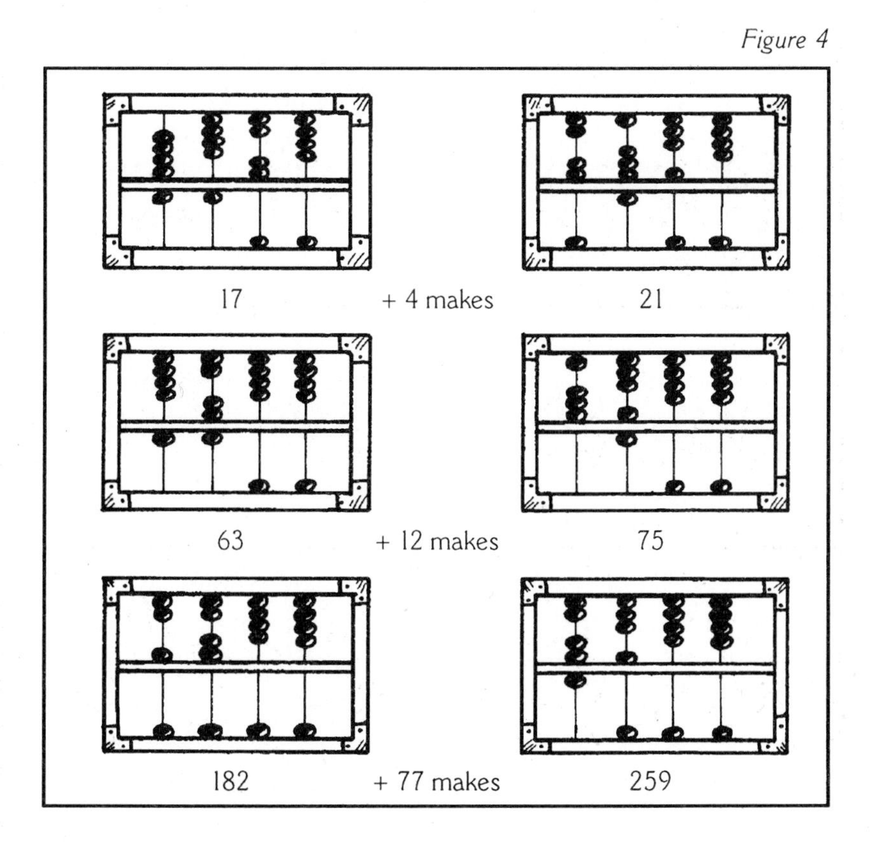

The problem:	31 – 4	32 – 4	33 – 4	34 – 4	35 – 4	36 – 4	37 – 4	38 – 4	39 – 4	40 – 4
The movements: remove (–) or add (+) tens	– 10	– 10	– 10							– 10
remove (–) or add (+) fives	+ 5	+ 5	+ 5		– 5	– 5	– 5	– 5		+ 5
remove (–) or add (+) ones	+ 1	+ 1	+ 1	– 4	+ 1	+ 1	+ 1	+ 1	– 4	+ 1
The result:	27	28	29	30	31	32	33	34	35	36

Figure 5

method, look at how 4 is subtracted from all the numbers between 31 and 40. (See Figure 5.) Remember how the numbers are represented on the abacus – for example, 36 is represented by three beads in a 10 column, one bead worth 5 and one bead worth 1 in a singles or units column.

Children who acquire the ability to manipulate symbols may be viewing the symbols in metonymic relation to the calculations to be performed, seeing the symbols as if they were real objects to be manipulated. Walkerdine (1988) describes young children working on tens and units calculations in this way; in preference to the use of metaphoric representation of numbers (in Walkerdine's study, these were bundles of matchsticks provided by the teacher and intended for use by the children as representations of tens and units).

Within the Anglo-Saxon culture, there is no recent historical equivalent of the abacus. Much of the equipment used in schools is seen as being exclusively for school use. Thus Dienes blocks are only found in classrooms, whereas the abacus was (and still is, in many countries) an everyday appliance for performing complex calculations.

Neither is there a climate of acceptance, within the dominant cultural tradition, of what might be termed 'body counting' – for instance, the use of fingers. However, young children are eager to produce rhythms and patterns through physical movement. Adeptness with hand-held computer toys is an example of this ability. The teaching of numeracy seldom makes use of children's interest in physical movement. Children in many British schools are expected to acquire numeracy skills without any opportunity to develop kinaesthetic and visual memory of simple routines where objects such as beads are manipulated. Instead, they are introduced to the algorithmic processes for calculation through the use of structured apparatus which is intended to illustrate metaphorically how the place value system and various algorithms work. They are expected to acquire a conceptual understanding of the place value system in a static context – and from this, to see how they should use and apply it.

In some British schools, children's use of fingers as an aid to counting is often denigrated by adults. It is frequently interpreted as a sign of children *not* having acquired the appropriate knowledge and skills. Fortunately, some children find creative solutions. One girl, whom I met in a Cardiff school where using fingers was seen as a clear sign of failure, had managed a convenient and effective solution to this prohibition. In answer to my question 'Well then, how do you manage when you can't use your fingers?' she gave the conspiratorial reply: 'I use my teeth!' She demonstrated briefly by touching her teeth in sequence with her tongue, and at the same time nodding her head and sub-vocally counting a sequence. She was not to be defeated!

INVENTED NUMBER SYSTEMS

> He told me that in 1886 he had invented an original system of numbering... his first stimulus was... his discomfort at the fact that the famous thirty-three gauchos of Uruguayan history should require two signs and two words, in place of a single word and a single sign. He then applied this absurd principle to the other numbers.
>
> Borges (1964: pp 92-93)

When a bump on the head renders him unable to forget anything, irrespective of its complexity, Borges' character Ireneo Funes creates a numbering system, every element of which he can recall at will. It comprises common words as referents for numbers.

> In place of seven thousand thirteen, Maximo Perez; in place of seven thousand fourteen, The Railroad, other numbers were, Luis Melian Lafinur, Olimar, sulphur... In place of five hundred he would say *nine*.

In examining the number system of one's own culture, it can be uncomfortable to realise that this system is neither fixed nor immutable. It has not been determined from within the world of mathematics, but has a certain temporariness and owes its continued usage more to social agreement than to laws of nature.

One can imagine an emergent community recognising the need to count accurately the days between harvest and sowing in order to maximise the chance of a successful crop. Accurate counting under these conditions is important and must follow a distinctive pattern. But naming the numbers is a different matter, and Funes pushes the naming process to absurdity.

Catherine Stern explores the same ground. She offers children an alternative system for naming the counting numbers. Thereby, she hopes to develop the children's awareness of the structure of the number system (Stern, 1953). Stern invites the children to begin afresh by playing a renaming game with the first ten counting numbers (from 1 to 10 and excluding zero). She provides ten apparently nonsensical syllables as substitutes: lah, ler, bye, bay, bee, lo, li, pop, ta, boo.

Work with colleagues Nigel Williams and Henry Liebling over the last few years has led us to develop the following activity with children and student teachers. Using Stern's ten new number names, the students are asked to generate names for numbers beyond ten. They have to present their findings in different ways. They can choose to use hand and body movements, spoken words, or written signs and symbols. They are also asked to teach the rest of the group some simple calculations based on the use of their invented method.

Later, the group studies the Arabic place value system in detail, and looks at systems from other cultures. From knowledge that already existed within each group, we have learned how to form counting patterns in Chinese, French, Italian, Malaysian and Welsh (among others). A playful interlude, this activity helps to illustrate some of the consequences of using counting systems which incorporate place value and systems which do not. It offers an opportunity to study the pattern breaks that exist in various systems – for example, in the French number system, a break from grouping in tens to grouping in twenties occurs after *soixante* and is accentuated at *quatre-vingt*. This topic receives considerable attention in Menninger (1969).

GIANTS AND TINY PEOPLE

As with teachers, not all children appreciate an abrupt welcome to mathematics via a route which accentuates logical, analytical activity. Maths is usually employed in studying the world of facts; but it can also be used to good effect to explore fiction. What teachers are likely to see here is the important issue of context. However, this section explores a further issue: the use of narrative. I want to use this word in three ways, to refer to:

1. In the broadest sense, all accounts that we tell of ourselves and others; all reported occurrences that concern us.
2. Stories, legends and myths, both spoken and written.
3. The activity of the teacher, who is constructing meaning within the classroom through language, gestures, mood – indeed, through everything that is transmitted to children during the teaching process.

Narrative can be thought of as a stitching process (a phrase borrowed from Lacan: *le point de capiton*).[4] We stitch different experiences together using narrative and we use the resulting fabric to describe 'ourselves'. Indeed the fabric that we stitch through our self-produced narratives is what constitutes 'us'. We describe, explain and locate ourselves in the narrative that tells of our experiences. Even very young children have no difficulty in constructing narrative accounts which they use to define themselves as individuals. In this sense, the idea of narrative is linked to the idea of identity.

With this in mind, we can look at some possible uses of Roald Dahl's story *The BFG*. This narrative can be used by teachers to involve children in mathematical thinking. Broadly speaking, this narrative 'hook' works in three ways.

First, children intuitively recognise narrative as a powerful device – even if they cannot stand outside it and objectify it as a process. (At least one branch of the 'Philosophy and Children' movement finds the use of story books and videos a powerful vehicle for helping children to explore fundamental questions and ideas.)[5]

Second, children's ability to identify consistency (and to spot inconsistency) within narrative is extremely well developed. Even very young children can recognise whether a narrative is internally consistent. Try telling a story or showing pictures 'out of sequence' (for example, making a character older, then younger again), and a reaction is almost guaranteed. In contrast, children's ability to spot inconsistency in their formal school mathematics is comparatively weak and develops much later. By providing a narrative and asking children to stitch the mathematics into it, we can use their ability to maintain consistency in non-mathematical narrative to help check the mathematics that they have been asked to construct.[6]

Third, legends and folklore surrounding giants and tiny people have played a significant part in the lives of people in many cultures and at many times. A wealth of cultural resources underlies their meaning as symbols. Giants therefore make an ideal subject for storytelling in classrooms. The giant is often a metaphor for a powerful force, whether good or evil; and stories about giants and tiny people offer an opportunity for children to explore their own feelings of vulnerability or omnipotence.[7]

When he first developed this activity, Nigel Williams presented children in his class with a cut-out of the giant's handprint, taken from the window soon after the BFG had found Sophie. The children were invited to comment on the cut-out hand before deciding on some mathematics work they would like to undertake. I used this activity during demonstration lessons with children aged from nine to eleven, observed by postgraduate student teachers. I did have to field a few questions about the authenticity of the 'giant' handprint; but the children's talk quickly moved on from scepticism, and they began to dwell on the fantastic and its conjunction with the mathematical. What is it possible to say about the BFG from the evidence of one handprint?

VARIATIONS THAT HAVE PRODUCED FURTHER MATHEMATICAL WORK

On one occasion, rather than photo-enlarge a hand, I drew the outline rather clumsily. After a considerable amount of work, the solemn conclusion of one studious group of girls was that this was *not* the hand of a giant. For a brief moment I anticipated the reason being that giants didn't exist; but I was delighted with the argument they presented. The proportion of the thumb to the fingers was unlike any they had previously encountered, and wasn't at all similar to the thumb-and-finger proportions to be found in the group of children in their class. From the evidence they had so far gathered, they argued that the cut-out hand was fake.

A consequence of photocopying one's own hand palm-down is that children may quite quickly start to examine finger and palm prints, recognising similarities and differences between hands.

A photo-enlargement of a baby's hand retains an unmistakable podgy and child-like appearance, providing a clear example of the distinction between *growth* and *development*. Some children find this worth pursuing: do giants have babies too? What would a baby giant look like? Would it look like a giant baby?

Is it possible to estimate with any confidence how tall the giant might be, based on the evidence of the handprint? Could we make a shoe for this giant? What about a belt, or some spectacles? Could the BFG get into the classroom – walking, crawling, through a door, through a window?

Ratio is a necessary part of any mathematical exploration of these questions. Some teachers may prefer to do some work on this topic before the arrival of the BFG, so that the children already have some of the necessary skills and knowledge. There are many possible questions which can help children to engage in ratio problems. For example, is it true that:

✧ you are as tall as your reach (arms stretched out sideways, reach measured from fingertip to fingertip);

✧ twice round your neck is the same distance as once round your waist;

✧ you are as tall as nine of your hands (measured from fingertip to wrist); and

✧ your foot length is the same as the distance between your wrist and the inside of your elbow?

Are your findings generally true for the people in this class?

The children have a choice of starting points, and could begin an investigation immediately. If some of the ideas are new to them, then the teacher could give a structured lesson along the following lines.

The children work as a teacher-led class on one of the above questions before splitting into groups and choosing a further question for themselves. Agree to work on a particular question, such as 'Is it true you are as tall as nine of your hands?' Encourage the children to make a very quick 'guesstimate' of the ratio for their own body. Have plenty of sticky labels available. If each child writes their estimate on one of these, the labels can be stuck onto a wall above a horizontal paper line (prepared by the teacher beforehand) which extends as far along the wall as possible. When all the children have committed themselves to guesstimates, invite discussion about the estimates and the strategies used to arrive at them. This may reveal strategies ranging from wild guesswork and copying friends' ideas to some considered doubling, halving and approximating.

Next, direct the discussion towards the need for a scale. This can produce useful talk about maximum and minimum numbers, ranges and intervals. Once it is decided upon, the scale can be put onto the horizontal line using sticky labels with numbers written in a bold colour. In ones and twos, the children then bring out their estimate labels and place them above the horizontal axis. When placed, these labels give the teacher and the children visual evidence of the *distribution* of estimates. The teacher has thus:

✧ modelled some useful procedures for investigating the problem;
✧ introduced some terminology relevant to data handling;
✧ encouraged estimates and helped children to use and communicate useful strategies such as halving, doubling, rounding and approximating;
✧ monitored the performance of individual children;
✧ instituted class discussions about useful strategies;
✧ constructed a wall display which can be referred to in further work.

The lesson can continue with the children working in groups. Suppose the original question was 'How many of your hands tall do you think you are?' The wall display now shows the range of estimated answers. Children need to carry out some practical work to measure their height in hands in order to check the accuracy of their estimates. They can record the actual measurement on a second label. The lesson may stop here, since children will take different periods of time to complete this practical work.

When they meet again, the teacher can continue with a class lesson. Each child now sticks a second label below the horizontal axis on the wall display. The two sets of results can be compared: the estimates above and the actual results below. The second set is likely to be much more compressed than the first. The teacher may need to prompt a number of discussions:

✧ What do we do with several results of the same value (e.g. five children producing a label with 8 as their ratio)?

✧ What do we do [where figures are to be rounded to the nearest whole number] with answers like eight and a bit, nearly nine or 8¾?

The point here is to extend rather than shorten the debate – to get the children to reason and suggest, rather than be told what to do.[8] The data obtained can be represented graphically in order to answer the original question (see Figure 6).

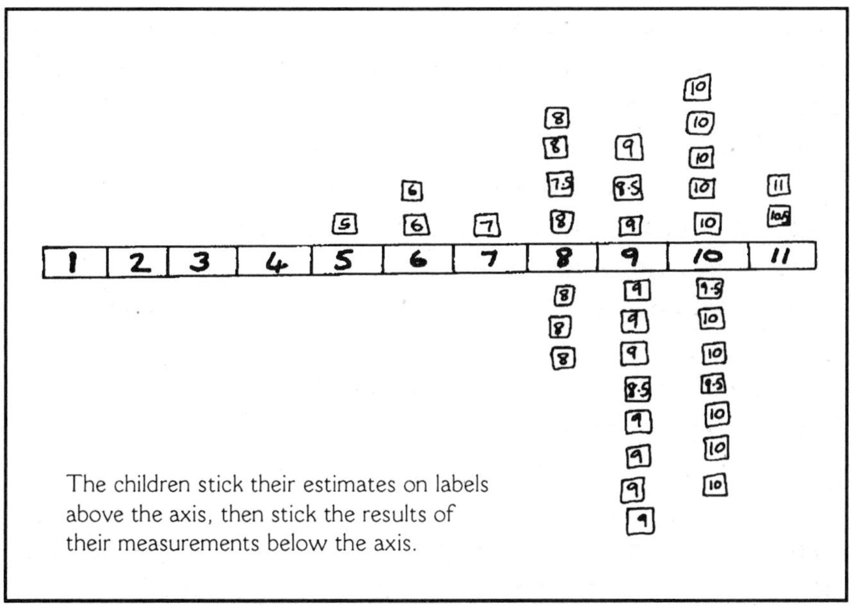

The children stick their estimates on labels above the axis, then stick the results of their measurements below the axis.

Figure 6

The children are now in a position to explore further ideas. They could make different items of clothing to fit the BFG. There will have to be consistency between different children's work if, for example, a sock and a shoe are to fit the same foot, or glasses and a hat to fit the same head.

ATTENTION AND EMOTION

Our focus of attention is not always that which is within our gaze. Attention is often directed by emotion, no less when learning mathematics than at other times. Imagine someone parking their cherished car overnight outside their home. On waking up they go to the window to admire it, but find it gone. It has been stolen during the night. As they gaze out of the window, another driver parks in their parking space. This example was used in a talk on attachment by the Buddhist nun Norden. The point of Norden's story is that while both people may be looking at a space between two parked vehicles, what they actually *see* is very different. Where one person sees an available parking space, the other sees the absence of a specific car. The difference in the focus of attention between the two people is influenced by their emotions. Teachers also help children to shift their focus of attention, and some of these shifts involve the force of emotion.

In Alison Reid's perceptive account (see page 129) of a teaching practice lesson, she observes Andrea working with Cuisenaire rods and notices that she is able to shift her attention so that she becomes more efficient at the task set. Some shifts of attention are the result of purposeful decisions, but many are not; indeed, many shifts of attention pass unnoticed until something causes us to reflect on them. In consequence, our ability to see, notice and observe is constantly in flux. Teachers have to learn how to perform their role within a space that occupies not only the gaze of the learner, but also the learner's focus of attention.

> When children work at mathematics, one looks at the way in which they participate. Some may know the rules but in their endeavours we see they do not enjoy. They have not been drawn

> in to the spirit of the activity. They cannot choose to play the game for whatever reason. We are distracted by the absence in their presence.
>
> Winnicott D.W. (1971)

Gaze and attention are both subject to shifting emotions, and teaching which ignores emotion ignores a powerful influence on learners. Effective teachers of mathematics teach learners how to shift the focus of their attention, and show them how to hold a new focus so that productive learning can take place. They help learners to notice what was previously unnoticed. Effective teaching involves altering the learner's awareness; it is all too easy to provide the mathematics and yet fail to provide for the learner. Effective teachers can recognise the 'absence in the presence' and respond positively by offering children routes to re-engagement.

USING STRUCTURED APPARATUS

The use of structured apparatus can serve both to hold children's attention and to act as a catalyst in shifting levels of awareness. In Alison Reid's account, both the children and Alison herself experience such a shift.

Alison's story[9]

On teaching practice I was in a Reception–Year 2 class. On this particular day my focus and teaching group of four children, Reception and Y1, were working with Cuisenaire rods. The tasks I set the children I had adapted from Holt (1964). The children had five minutes of exploratory play with the rods while I organised the rest of the class. After this I stayed with the group for the greater part of the maths session. To begin with I asked the children to find the rod which is the same length as two white rods. All four children in the group had no trouble doing this. They placed the red rod and the two white rods together in front of them. They then found the rod which is the same length as three white rods. We moved on when I was satisfied that they were happy dealing with the rods and their different values. I next asked the children to find the rod that is the same length as nine white rods. I asked them to put two of these rods in front of them together with one rod that was the same as six whites sandwiched in between. [See Figure 7.] They could then hold them up and clearly see the gap left between the blue rods at the end of the green one. I asked, 'Can you find the rod that fits the space?' Later, we tried various other combinations of sandwiched rods. To begin with all four children appeared to be approaching the task by trial and error: picking up a rod that seemed to be the right length and trying it. After a couple of attempts, one of the Reception children, Andrea, began to pick up the correct rod every time. She would look at the rods in front of her for slightly longer than the other children before choosing the correct rod to fill the gap. She seemed to be working it out. One of the Y1 children was engrossed in the task, working quickly and sometimes ahead of the rest. While I was working with the others at one point he called out, 'Look, eight is the same as two fours!' This was something he had never been able to do before. The children were doing quite complex calculations that they would have found very difficult or impossible to do on paper. Six and something makes nine. Three and something makes nine. Four is the same as two and two, etc. Andrea went on to do some independent work with the rods. She made a long train of rods that were all the same length as the blue rod. Each train consisted of two or three rods, e.g. a purple and a yellow, light green with a red and a purple. She even managed to go on to record her work by writing down each combination of rods in numerals, e.g. 5 + 4 = 9.

The value of the rods is that the children can actually see what the numbers represent, instead of having to translate numerals. They can actually 'measure' that two fours are the same as eight. The rods have a graphic and practical quality that is precious. As well as this valuable learning experience, the rods offer a practical activity that has flexibility for both independent learning and teacher-led tasks. This I found very useful.

Alison Reid (1996)

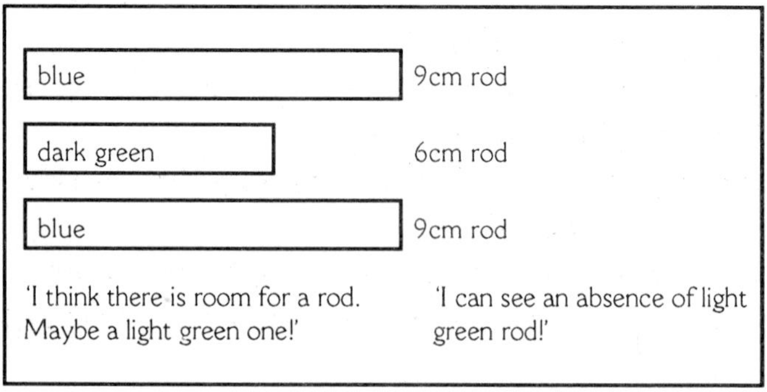

blue	9cm rod
dark green	6cm rod
blue	9cm rod

'I think there is room for a rod. Maybe a light green one!'

'I can see an absence of light green rod!'

Figure 7

What excites me in Alison's account is Andrea's shift of attention from an absence of rod to a perception of the space as an appropriate place for a light green rod. I now have an additional way of working with children, using Alison's 'rod sandwiches'. I can say to them: 'Look at the empty space. Now imagine a rod there. What colour is the rod you are imagining? Find your rod and check.'

Physical manipulation of rods allows children to model problems and construct metaphors of mathematical situations. The use of rods has a social impact too. The timespan between teacher question and pupil answer is well-researched and of extremely short duration. Eye contact between teacher and pupil serves to shorten this even further. Looking away is often judged to be impolite: 'Look at me when I'm talking to you!' Thinking can be hampered by continual eye contact. 'I can't think straight when you look at me like that!' The introduction of a physical object (such as rods) between teacher and pupil introduces a legitimate alternative focus, allowing eye contact to be broken (or avoided) and thinking to continue. Thinking can also be supported, of course, by the manipulation of the rods when the children are familiar with them.

It is possible that some children who cease to depend on the rods as an aid to calculation do so because they have developed flexible visual images of the rods, which they can manipulate without needing the rods to be present. This may take some time, and cannot be rushed. However, it may be possible for teachers to model the process with further work in which the rods can be imagined. In this way, children are given opportunities to strengthen their ability to develop and hold visual images. It is not a competition; nor is it a race to dump the rods in favour of 'grown-up methods'.

✧ 'I'm thinking of two rods. Together they are as long as a pink. Which ones could I be imagining?'

✧ 'I'm thinking of a rod which is one red longer than a yellow. Which colour rod am I thinking of?'

✧ 'I'm thinking of a pair of rods whose difference in length is the same as a pink rod. Tell me some pairs of rods that I might be thinking of.'

✧ 'You imagine a yellow and a white. What rod is as long as these two together?'

Hiding games can also provide opportunities for strengthening mental images. A number line pinned to the wall with the numbers 1 to 6 visible, and the rest hidden by a paper cloud or going into a tunnel entrance suggests continuation and provokes discussion ('What numbers do you think are hidden?') Hiding games which involve counting imagined objects also force the attention onto algebraic relationships. Children can count a small number of objects, which are then hidden by a cloth. Some objects are then brought out from under the cloth and into view, so that the children can count them. How many objects remain hidden under the cloth? Knowledge of arithmetic is necessary but insufficient here, since the algebra of the situation has to be considered before a mental calculation can be made.

In these examples, a mathematical situation is being *modelled*. There is a movement, actual or implied, which involves a transformation according to an algebraic rule; the movement invokes (or evokes) the rule. What emerges here is a 'coming to know' which is supported by visual, imagined and kinaesthetic experiences. Structured apparatus is particularly valuable in supporting this internalisation of mathematical relationships through visual and kinaesthetic modelling.

MATHEMATICS, PSYCHODYNAMICS AND EDUCATION THERAPY

Mathematics is highly prized in the workplace, but is under-represented in terms of the number of people who seek qualifications. There is a strong antipathy towards discussing it – especially in public. Many people are eager to deny mathematical competence, which is associated with influential and unhelpful stereotypes. Mathematics and the study of mathematics carry a strongly negative emotional charge.[10]

A traditional notion of mathematics is that of an external body of knowledge with rules and relationships that are generalised, highly symbolic and context-free. A quite different idea which has received considerable attention in recent years portrays mathematics as permeating the internalised world of our unconscious thoughts.

According to this view, maths is 'sticky' and mathematical knowledge can become firmly attached to some of the material in the unconscious mind. Unconscious thoughts can then be explored through the mathematics that has become attached to them.

The work of the Centre Medico-Psycho-Pedagogique Claude-Bernard has continued since its formation in 1946. Its workers are committed to a holistic approach to the child and the family, and much of their work involves helping pupils with the learning of mathematics and with what might be represented by their particular failure to learn. Weyl-Kailey (1985) gives a number of accounts of work with pupils using an approach similar to that which Caspari (1978) describes as *education therapy* and which has been developed by Barrett and Trivett (1991).

With Carole, an eleven-year-old girl whose parents worked in the diplomatic service, constant travelling had created problems. Carole's parents were of different nationalities (Scandinavian and Italian). She had attended school in France for eighteen months without difficulty. Problems arose when she transferred from *septième* to *sixième* at the beginning of a new academic year. She completely failed to achieve, and she showed high levels of anxiety. In mathematics, though she was proficient in number work, she failed totally to understand work in sets and set theory. Weyl-Kailey began work with Carole using plastic animals of different colours. Carole was soon able to sort and group these using different criteria – though she was resistant to recording any of the work. Playing with the animals helped her to regain some of her lost confidence. Though she remained generally nervous and anxious, she was able to explore the mathematics of sets (*le principe de l'appartenance*) – which, for Carole, carried a double meaning. After a number of meetings, Weyl-Kailey posed a key question which utterly astonished Carole.

> <<Et toi, à quel ensemble appartiens-tu?>> Elle me regarda très étonnée: <<Je n'appartiens à aucun ensemble! – Pourtant, tu es une fille? Tu fais donc partie de l'ensemble des filles... Ah! C'est vrai! – Et ne fais-tu pas partie de l'ensemble des élèves de

> sixième? – Vous croyez? – Tous les jeunes de ton âge ne sont pas en sixième.
>
> Weyl-Kailey (1985: p.183)[11]

They came, after some time, to the heart of Carole's anxiety: dual nationality. Gradually, after much delicate work, it was possible for her to enter – and subsequently to experience belonging within – the intersection of the two sets which represented those who are Scandinavian *and* those who are Italian. She began to see herself as belonging to both groups, rather than to neither. Weyl-Kailey linked Carole's sense of self to a mathematical metaphor. Carole intuitively sensed herself to be living in an intersection, the properties of which she defined as 'neither one nor the other'. She was eventually able to replace this isolated sense of self with the inclusive mathematical definition of 'belonging equally to both sets'.

Pimm (1994) recounts an experience with Katie, aged three, in which Katie hinted at the significance that numbers had for her. Following on from a conversation between Pimm and Katie's mother about miscounting people grouped round a meal table the previous night, Katie entered the conversation by pointing and counting. Pimm was to be one, Katie's mother was to be two, and Katie herself was also to be two. One, two, two. Then as an aside: 'I know it is one, two, three but I'm pretending.'

Pimm recalls:

> I then remember that, moments before this reckoning, Katie had remarked to me, 'Daddy dead.' Her father was killed not long after she was one. I also remember the night before this breakfast when she arrives home from childcare... she says to me 'I thought you were daddy.' ...It comes to me that 'three' was also what they were as a family before becoming two, and Katie was the third.
>
> Pimm (1994: p.120)

It is impossible to say what associations are formed in the unconscious between mathematics and experiences which raise disturbing contradictions or intense excitement. For Katie, we can guess that in her life the addition of two and one more did not follow the mathematical rules that applied in many other situations with which she was familiar. When an experience carries a powerful emotional charge it can be unconsciously stitched to our mathematical knowledge.

The diversity of ideas in this chapter reflects the diversity of play. Children's play combines physical activity and reflection. It incorporates real-life issues and developing social skills. It involves emotion and imagination. The teaching of numeracy needs to employ these resources.

In this chapter, I have offered some themes for exploration. I believe it is timely for all of us who teach mathematics to consider them. These narratives are intended to provoke an interpretation in the mind of the reader; they are offered in the spirit of Spencer (1982), who suggests that the ultimate reason for retaining an interpretation is that it is fruitful and offers possibilities.

NOTES

1. David (aged 6) was interviewed in school in 1983. He was playing with sticks and trying to make the numbers 3 to 7. He was enjoying this self-invented activity and was trying to develop a convention whereby he could use four sticks to represent 4, five to represent 5 and so on. In conversation he reported trying to make the numerals appear on his bedroom wall by staring at the wall and 'making the numbers come'. *Unpublished MPhil notes, Tony Brown.*
2. An account of an activity with four- and five-year-olds appears in Harrison, J. et al (1993).
3. See Mason (1986) for an elaboration.
4. For a detailed account of the application of some of Lacan's ideas to educational issues, see Atkinson, D. and Moore, A. (1994).
5. Murris, K. (1992) *Teaching Philosophy With Picture Books.*
6. See also Brown, T. (1996) 'Narrative and Mathematics'.
7. There are many stories of giants and tiny people which are suitable for use with children. Further activities based on stories could include the collection

and examination of everyday objects that a giant or a tiny person might find when visiting the classroom: nails, clothes pegs, a wicker-basket, toothpicks, kitchen roll, knives, forks or spoons. What would they make of these? How would each appear to a giant or to a tiny person? How might they use the objects?

8. The source of this idea was a workshop run by Janine Blinko, whose chosen activity was to ask for an estimate of the number of raisins in a small packet which each person had been given. This was followed by a count of the actual number contained in each packet.

9. Alison Reid presented her story during a college session where we were reviewing planning and teaching, following a teaching practice.

10. See: Burton, L. (1986) *Girls into maths can go*; Walden, R. & Walkerdine, V. et al (1985) *Girls and maths: from primary to secondary schooling*; Burton, L. (1990) *Gender and Maths*.

11. 'And you, which group do you belong to?'

She looked at me in great surprise. 'I don't belong to any group.'

'You're a girl, aren't you? Then you are one of the members of the group called girls.'

'Yes, that's true!'

'And aren't you a member of the group of children in Level Six? Do you believe that? Not all young people of your age are in Level Six.'

CHAPTER 8

ASSESSING NUMERACY

Current research in mathematics education confirms the importance of assessment as a part of teaching. Teachers are involved in both summative and formative assessments. This chapter concentrates on formative assessment; it investigates the importance of an ongoing evaluation of children's learning, and the dynamic relationship between assessment and planning. Assessment and the recording of collected evidence need to be integrated within everyday teaching.

CURRENT RESEARCH AND ITS IMPLICATIONS

The findings of current research in mathematics education have implications for assessment and its place in teaching. The brief summary below is taken from Askew, M. and Wiliam, D. (1995) *Recent Research in Mathematics Education 5–16* (OFSTED), and looks at early years, arithmetic methods, practical work and real contexts, misconceptions, the teacher's role, and the effect of assessment on children's learning.

EARLY YEARS

Young children's competence with number is often underestimated. Current research shows that children starting school bring with them a wealth of understanding about mathematics. The aim should be to find out what they know and understand and to plan the teaching from that, rather than assuming that they know nothing. Research shows that before they start school, many young children:

✧ can count and know what counting is for;
✧ use vocabulary such as 'more' and 'less' with understanding;
✧ have some practical understanding of addition and subtraction with small numbers;
✧ can find ways of tackling and solving problems.

However, children's understanding of this mathematics is not always what adults expect. Children may be able to count by reciting a sequence of numbers, but not to connect counting with finding the quantity. The teacher needs to find out, through assessment, exactly what children know about counting when they first come to school. The following analysis, developed by Sue Gifford in *Mathematics in the Primary School: A Sense of Progression* (1996), is useful for looking at the detailed assessments which are needed at this stage:

Key ideas	Assessment points
Counting	Saying numbers in order. One number for each object.
Cardinality	'So how many are there?'
Counting for a purpose	Counting, not grabbing. Counting to check.
Comparing	Use 'more' and 'less'. Using numbers to compare.
Representing numbers	Using tallies or numerals.
Reading numbers	Saying the numbers. Referring to the numeral to check the number there should be.
Addition and subtraction	Using visualisation or fingers with a range of numbers. Knowing number bonds. 'How did you work it out?'
Multiplication and division	Counting groups as items. Sharing equally. Knowing number facts, e.g. 4 between 2 means 2 each.

ARITHMETIC METHODS 7–12

Children who know some number facts by heart, and are able to deduce other number facts because of their understanding of the relationship between numbers, make more progress because each approach supports the other. Deducing number facts helps children to commit more facts to memory, and recalled facts help to expand the range of strategies for deriving more facts. The implication for assessment is that testing children's knowledge of number facts only tells us part of the story. We also need to assess their ability to tackle new problems and to derive solutions. One way of doing this is to develop children's flexibility in mental mathematics through class and group discussions on a daily basis, and to make sharing ideas about mental methods a basis for debate in the classroom. Assessments can readily be made in these sessions.

Another aspect of this particular set of findings concerned low-attaining pupils. Some low-attaining children depend heavily on counting methods, which can get them slowly to a correct answer. But often, these remove the need to commit number facts to memory, and this will hamper the children's ability to tackle problems and derive solutions. If there is evidence that children are relying on counting methods, you can plan sets of strategies to encourage them to work from remembered facts instead. An example might be a child who, when adding the scores of two dice, always counts both sets of spots. You could cover one dice with your hand and encourage counting on from a known number, or provide one dice with numerals and the other with spots.

PRACTICAL WORK

When children use practical apparatus to solve and model some calculation problems, it does not follow that they automatically develop an understanding of the abstract concepts. This research indicates that practical tasks and abstract ideas each need to be explored in their own right, and that we need to have considerable discussion with children about the links between them. An example here might be using base ten apparatus to model subtraction by decomposition. That children can use the apparatus to solve the problems does not necessarily mean that they understand the formal process. Assessment of their understanding needs to be probed with discussion.

MISCONCEPTIONS

Research on children's misconceptions confirms what we might expect: that children learn by their mistakes as long as those mistakes are looked at, unpicked and discussed in teaching. There are certain misconceptions in mathematics that are widespread among children, and it would seem important for children's learning to go through the process of having these misconceptions, then working through them. Thus it is not helpful to teach in a way that prevents children from creating any misconceptions. But equally clearly, the misconceptions need to be addressed by effective questioning and discussion. Again, this involves constant assessment of children's mathematical ideas.

We need to develop a way of analysing children's errors in mathematics so that we can find out where their misconceptions lie. The children's recording is a good starting point for analysis. Listening to their statements and discussions is another.

THE TEACHER'S ROLE: QUESTIONING

Effective questioning by teachers can raise children's achievement in mathematics. It can also help teachers to discover what children know and understand. Effective questions can be classified as 'higher-level' questions, and questions that are less effective as 'low-level'. An example of a low-level question is '$3 \times 2 = \square$'; an example of a higher-level question is 'Tell me all the pairs of numbers you can find which multiply to give 6'. Clearly, higher-level questions are more useful for assessment because they elicit fuller information from the child.

THE EFFECT OF ASSESSMENT ON CHILDREN'S LEARNING

Research shows that assessment has a strong influence, both on teachers and on children. Assessments give children a clear idea of what teachers value, and this can motivate children – though it can also have negative consequences. Research in the USA has shown that over-reliance on standardised achievement tests can have a negative effect on the quality of teaching. It was found that teachers neglect the assessment of individual children and pay more attention to whole-class results, teaching only with those in mind. This narrows the focus of the teaching, and does not give teachers information about the progress and teaching needs of individuals. Children may perceive that schoools only value learning that is tested. Research also shows that teachers are better at assessing high-attaining children than low attainers, and are more accurate in judging computational skills than mathematical concepts.

WHAT IS ASSESSMENT?

Assessment is the process of gathering evidence about a child's knowledge of, ability to use, and attitude towards a subject. Our main reason for gathering all this evidence is that we can use it to help children progress with their learning. The evidence helps us by informing our teaching. If we know what children have learned and understood, we can decide what to teach them next.

It seems an odd thing to say, but assessment helps us to distinguish between teaching and learning! Inconveniently, and against all our reckoning, children do not necessarily learn what we teach them. Research by Brenda Denvir (see Askew & Wiliam, 1995) found that children who were taught specific mathematical ideas quite often *learned* something completely different. The children continued their learning about numbers, but they made connections that were not intended by the teacher. The lesson here is that when we teach children, we need to build in a way of finding out what they have learned, so that we know how to continue.

There are other reasons for making assessments. There is a legal requirement to test aspects of children's knowledge in mathematics at the end of each Key Stage with standard assessment tasks, in order to make national comparisons, and in order to report results to parents. Assessment of children's performance in mathematics is a part of the public accountability of teachers and schools, to make sure that children throughout the UK are being educated adequately. The extent to which these legal requirements and the means by which they are enforced ultimately contribute to children's learning is an issue of current debate in education.

It is clear, however, that assessing children's learning in mathematics must have a practical function apart from the legal one. Assessment for its own sake does not advance children's learning. There is a saying: 'Weighing the pig doesn't make it grow'. Finding out that a child can count to 100 does not help the child learn more, unless as a teacher you use that knowledge to develop the child's understanding of numbers.

DIFFERENT KINDS OF ASSESSMENT

(I) SUMMATIVE ASSESSMENT

Summative assessments provide a snapshot summary of a child's progress in mathematics. They are usually arrived at by testing children. The national Key Stage 1 and Key Stage 2 assessments are summative tests which have been standardised in order to be suitable for a particular age-group, to follow an agreed national standard of achievement, and to allow the results to be used in comparing educational achievement in different schools and regions. Some schools use summative tests provided commercially, or written by teachers, which are used at the end of a block of work or at certain times in the school year. The results of these tests are used within the school. Summative tests are useful for finding out whether a whole class (or school) has difficulty with one area of mathematics learning, such as data handling, or solving word problems. The school can then make plans to develop that area of work more thoroughly. It is important for teachers to use the information gained from summative assessment in their teaching plans.

Summative assessment has a specific role, but it is important to bear in mind its limitations:

- ✧ The questions about knowledge of facts can only sample; they can't test all knowledge. Because a child knows 7×7, it doesn't mean he or she knows 8×7.
- ✧ The tests generally test only those things that can be written down in short answers. They don't test skills in problem solving, imagery and visualising, discussion of mathematical ideas, practical tasks and so on.
- ✧ There can be a tendency to over-emphasise the tests' importance, and to plan teaching around the narrower skills that the tests require.
- ✧ The tests do not allow for children's own individual style of working and patterns of learning.
- ✧ Account cannot be taken of children's performance in a particular test. Some children may work slowly, have 'off' days or make atypical mistakes.
- ✧ The tests don't provide enough information to probe a child's understanding.

(II) FORMATIVE ASSESSMENT

The most important form of assessment consists of the professional judgements that teachers make daily in the course of their teaching. Assessment informs every other part of a teacher's work. The starting point for planning is knowing where children have got to and what they have achieved. Teachers make judgements about how well children are doing in a task, and that helps them in deciding how and what to teach. Children, in general, respond enthusiastically and confidently to discussions of how they are getting on and what they have achieved – assessment is important to children as well as to teachers. Formative assessment involves the piecing together of planned and incidental assessments to plan and provide for the successful learning of each child.

(III) DIAGNOSTIC ASSESSMENT

There are times when the teacher needs to focus on the particular skills, knowledge or understanding that a child has, in order to find out exactly what he or she can do or understand in that area. An example of a broad approach to diagnostic assessment is starting some work on place value with a group of children and wanting to know exactly what their understanding of this principle is. The teacher can set them an activity which is designed to 'diagnose' where they are in that area of mathematics, and what work the teacher needs to plan.

However, diagnostic assessment is more usually related to individual children's learning. For example, the teacher may notice over a period of time that a child reverses numbers and counts in an odd way, and therefore suspect that there may be a problem with sequencing. The teacher can develop specific activities and questions to probe the child's understanding, and to try and identify his or her misconceptions. Or the teacher may notice that a child has an exceptional grasp of 3D space, and try to determine the full extent of that understanding by making a diagnostic assessment. Often, making a diagnostic assessment requires the involvement of professionals outside the school; and it can lead to a child requiring special teaching.

KEY VOCABULARY USED WITH ASSESSMENT

Concepts	General and fundamental mathematical ideas.
Context	The circumstances or situation in which a mathematical problem occurs, or in which mathematics can be applied.
Evaluation	The process of determining the worth of, or assigning a value to, something on the basis of careful examination and judgement.
Open-ended questions	Tasks that allow for various acceptable answers and for multiple approaches to finding an effective solution.
Outcomes	Learning, results or consequences.
Skills	Abilities in performing routine mathematical procedures, typically using computation or apparatus.
Standardised test	A test that is administered, scored and interpreted in a consistent manner, whenever and to whomever it is given.

WHAT ASSESSMENT INVOLVES

Assessment is a complex process that needs thought and planning (like everything else in teaching). Let's unpick the process to see what is involved. Assessment can be either summative or formative, formal or informal, planned or incidental. There should be overall plans for the use of assessment; thought should be given to the evidence the assessment provides, how that evidence is interpreted, and how the results will be used. A diagram is useful here:

Planning for assessment

⇩

Gathering evidence

⇩

Evaluating the evidence

⇩

Acting on the evidence

We can use a checklist of questions to clarify these processes:

(1) PLANNING FOR ASSESSMENT

	Example 1 Multiplication tables	Example 2 Place value
What is the assessment for?	To find out if all the children in the class know the multiplication tables.	To find out how a particular group of children understands place value.
Why do I want to know?	To plan how much more practice to give some or all of the children, as part of the work on knowledge of number facts.	To know where to start the planned work on place value with the children.
What sort of assessment is appropriate: formal or informal?	Formal.	Informal.
Should the assessment be planned or incidental?	Planned.	Planned.
How will I find out what I want to know?	Give the class a written test.	Plan an activity, and plan questions to ask the children (both as a group and as individuals).
What criteria will I use?	Right and wrong answers. Speed of response. Analysis of wrong answers for patterns of misconceptions.	Whether the children can group objects into groups of ten, and whether they can answer my specific questions seeking clarification on what they have done.
How will I record the evidence?	On a prepared tick list.	I will only record evidence of unexpected understanding or misunderstanding in specific children. If this is contained on a child's piece of recording, I will make notes on that and keep it simple.

GATHERING EVIDENCE

	Example 1	Example 2
How did I choose the activities?	Provided by the published scheme used in the school.	From the school scheme of work, in the section on place value relevant to my year group.
How are the children involved in the assessment?	The children have agreed that they need to know multiplication facts, and that this test is part of monitoring their progress.	The children know that they are doing some work on place value. They expect to discuss the work they do.
What system of record-keeping do I have for this assessment?	A checklist for the class of the key number facts I want the children to learn.	A prepared sheet for the group showing the learning objectives for the activity, on which I can record any observations I make (if any).

(III) EVALUATING THE EVIDENCE

	Example 1	Example 2
What specific evidence am I looking for?	I am looking for correct answers, but I am also looking for patterns of wrong answers to spot children's misconceptions.	Can the children group in tens? Can they talk about groups of tens and ones? Can they write two-digit numbers correctly? Can they tackle a problem? Can they discuss the mathematics appropriately.
How do I evaluate the evidence?	I use the result of the test as a rough measure of the range of knowledge and multiplication facts in the class. I know that children's performance in these tests can be patchy, and that I will need a different method to find out in more depth some children's knowledge and understanding of multiplication.	I use my own understanding of the development of children's learning in place value to decide on the questions to ask children, and on my interpretation of their responses.

What understanding will I gain about the children's learning?	I will know which children remembered certain number facts at the time of the test. I do not expect to learn anything about the children's understanding of numbers unless I question them afterwards about which numbers they remembered and which they calculated.	I hope to gain a good insight into the children's understanding of place value. I will continue to learn about each child's attitude towards and confidence in mathematics.

(IV) ACTING ON THE EVIDENCE

	Example 1	Example 2
Will the results be recorded in any way?	In my own informal class records.	Most of the information I will keep in my head, because I have a clear overview of all the subjects I am assessing. I may keep some notes about specific children, and I may keep significant annotated pieces of work.
What action will I take as a result of the assessments I have made?	I will plan games and activities involving the use and learning of number facts (at an appropriate level) for groups of children. I will investigate any misconceptions with more specific and in-depth assessments.	I will modify the plans I have made to teach place value at an appropriate level for this group, and pick up on specific teaching points that have arisen for my next lesson. I will note these modifications in my planning diary.

PLANNED ASSESSMENT

Planning and assessment are inextricably linked. A school's scheme of work not only identifies aspects of mathematics to be learned and the learning objectives, it also contains methods of assessment for those learning objectives. A useful way of organising a scheme of work is to take each mathematical topic and expand the programme of study across the range of levels, then detail the learning intentions for each level, so that continuity and progression are clear. The programme of study should suggest good assessment activities for each key topic which are adaptable for two or three levels. We can take *place value* as an example:

KS1 Programme of Study	Learning objectives	Assessment activity
Read, write and order numbers, initially to 10, progressing up to 1000, developing an understanding that the position of a digit signifies its value; begin to approximate large numbers to the nearest 10 or 100.	✧ Can organise a number of objects into groups of ten and give the total, counting in tens and ones. ✧ Having organised objects as above, can write the total number. ✧ When shown a written number, can say how many sets of ten that number of objects would make, and how many objects would be left over.	*Checkpoints assessment cards:* Whole Numbers 4 (see page 40 of school assessment folder).
	✧ Can choose a number on a 0–100 number line and say how many jumps of 10 and steps of one it would take to reach that number from 0. ✧ Can say which number on a 0–100 number line they would reach after making a given number of jumps of 10 and steps of one from 0.	BEAM *Number at Key Stage 1:* page 52 'Stepping Stones' (see page 40 of school assessment folder).
	✧ Can mentally add 10 to any number. ✧ Can mentally subtract 10 from any number.	Photocopied activity (see page 42 of school assessment folder).
	✧ Can add a tens number and a single-digit number on a calculator to make a given two-digit number.	*Scholastic Maths Focus Kit 1 Book 3:* page 32 (see page 43 of school assessment folder).

The resources referred to above are:
Checkpoints assessment cards (ILEA 1980), AMS Educational, Leeds.
Number at Key Stage 1 (BEAM 1995).
Maths Focus Kit 1 Book 3 (Scholastic 1996).

The scheme of work will suggest a variety of other activities for place value, each of which will offer opportunities for assessment while the children are engaged in them. However, it is useful to have available either activities designed for a specific assessment or general activities that lend themselves to assessing particular learning objectives. Ideas and approaches for assessing children's understanding of a new topic are useful as well. Here is an example used by a teacher in one school; he successfully recommended it to others in the school, who included it in their scheme of work. It is important, of course, to make sure that you have thought about the mathematics involved before you give a task to the children in this way.

Ways of assessing children's knowledge of a new mathematical topic

Discuss the topic with the whole class.
Ask them to tell you everything they know about it.
Write each thing they tell you on the blackboard or on a flip chart.
Prepare (or have the children prepare) separate labels, each with one item on it.
The children work in pairs to sort and cluster these ideas on a sheet of A3 paper, and show links with any related ideas. They can add anything else they think of.
It becomes clear where the gaps in their thinking are.
As the topic progresses they can fill in new ideas and indicate which ideas they feel they understand.

In short-term planning, teachers use assessment evidence to make decisions about tomorrow, the day after, and next week. Planning involves reviewing what you want the children to learn and the current long-term plans, and reconsidering those plans in the light of information gathered about the children's learning on a day-to-day basis. Short-term plans could be modified, for example, where a lesson is not understood in the way you had expected: the next lesson might be changed to deal with this. Long-term plans could be modified, for example, where some planned work on addition and subtraction over three weeks reveals that a class needs more work on place value; you might decide to do that as the next block of work, instead of the planned work on fractions.

At the end of a block of work, you may feel that you need to make an overall assessment of the children's understanding so far; but most of the assessment will have been done as you go along. It is not possible to assess all outcomes for all children – but you will have been looking out for surprises and notable leaps of understanding, often termed 'significant achievement'.

To summarise, here are the planning principles that should underpin *all* lessons:

1. Plan specific learning objectives for the whole class, the group and the individual.
2. Consider the question 'Who is this for?' Is it for all, or some but not others? Will you need to differentiate?
3. The children do the activity. How will you make sure you have fulfilled the learning objectives?
4. What happens? Assess the children as they do the activity. Make the assessment there and then.
5. What next? Feed the evaluation into your planning; amend your short-term plans.

INCIDENTAL ASSESSMENT

Assessment does not just mark the beginning or end of a cycle of learning (a mathematics topic, the end of an exercise book, the end of term or the end of a Key Stage). Assessment that contributes to children's learning becomes an integral part of teaching that encourages and supports further learning. Opportunities for incidental assessment occur naturally in the classroom. They include listening to children, observing them, making sense of what they do and say. In planning, teachers can identify opportunities for a variety of assessments. It is helpful, in planning, to consider the following questions as a matter of course:

✧ What questions will I ask?

✧ What will I observe?

✧ Which activities will provide me with useful assessment points?

Activities that are best for incidental assessments are open-ended in some way: there may be a range of possible answers, or different methods that could be used, or ways of modifying the problem. Here are some examples of open-ended activities and assessments they could be used for:

Activity	Assessment points	Questions to ask
What different calculations can you make with the numbers 6, 4 and 8?	Do the children: ✧ use all the four rules signs, or do they just use addition and subtraction? ✧ use division, even though you've never taught it? ✧ work out sequences of calculations, such as a series of subtractions, showing a feeling for pattern? ✧ use two- and three-digit numbers? ✧ think creatively and use fractions, decimals, very large numbers? ✧ persist with and enjoy playing with numbers? and so on...	Can you think of any more like that one? Can you sort these out into calculations that are like each other in some way? Are there any operations you haven't used? Could you use two operations in one calculation? Or three?
How many objects in the jar?	Do the children: ✧ count the objects without missing any? ✧ know all the number names in sequence? ✧ organise their counting in some way? ✧ make a sensible estimate of how many objects they have to count? ✧ keep track of their counting if distracted? and so on...	How do you know you counted them all? What comes after 10? After 19? Can you think of a quicker way of counting? Can you count in twos? What other ways of counting can you use?

	Do the children: ✧ find a way of measuring the ball? ✧ estimate effectively the amount of paper/card needed for the task? ✧ plan ahead? ✧ make a net of the box? ✧ work out where to place flaps? ✧ make the box the right size? And so on...	How do you know this paper is big enough? How could you measure this with the ruler? When you fold it, which edge will this flap touch?

You can refine the assessment points for a particular age-group range of levels in your planning, and decide on the questions that will help you to probe children's understanding in a particular mathematical area.

Integrating assessment and teaching means making immediate decisions in lessons that can change the course of the lesson. We collect evidence about learning mostly by observing, listening and questioning. Posing appropriate questions is the most important way of collecting evidence for assessment while teaching. Research has shown that higher-order questions not only elicit more information than lower-order questions, they can also raise achievement. An

Figure 1

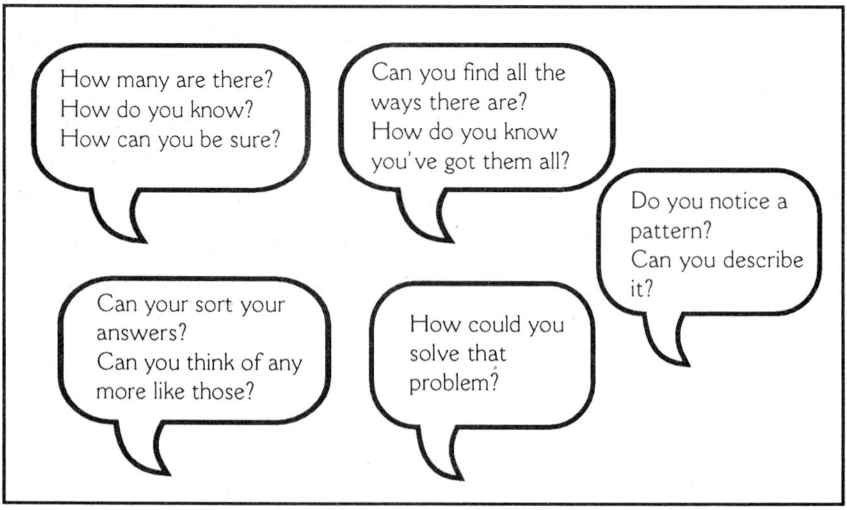

example of a low-level question is 'What is the name of this shape?' An example of a higher-level question is 'How would you describe this shape to a friend over the telephone so that she could draw a copy?'

Anita Straker, in her book *Talking Points in Mathematics*, gives a page of useful questions that can be asked at various stages of progress through a mathematical problem or activity. An armoury of such questions would be an invaluable inclusion in a scheme of work. With time and experience, these questions can become part of the teacher's repertoire. (See Figure 1.)

CHILDREN'S INVOLVEMENT IN ASSESSMENT

Children should be involved in assessments of their learning. It is only reasonable that children should know how they are to be assessed, what mathematics they will be expected to do, the criteria for judging their performance, and the consequences of the assessment (including future work to be done). They need to understand different forms of assessment and their purposes: what tests are for, the reasons for doing specific tests and how it helps your teaching, and ways of assessing themselves.

CONTEXTS FOR ASSESSMENT

Formative assessment should take place during all those contexts and social situations in which children learn and do mathematics. Some of these assessments will relate directly to the programmes of study in the relevant national curriculum, such as logical reasoning or knowledge of fractions. Other assessments will have to do with social ways of learning and attitudes towards mathematics. Here are some examples of contexts with suggestions about what should be assessed.

Listening

Understanding explanations

Carrying out instructions

Answering questions

Responding to answers

Reading

Reading numbers in a variety of everyday contexts

Using a set of instructions, such as a recipe

Following the rules of a game

Understanding a written problem in a textbook

Interpreting a poster or display

Comparing a friend's written record with your own

Following instructions on a computer

Writing

Writing numbers

Pencil and paper calculations

Drawings of patterns and shapes

Diagrammatic representations

Recording the working out of a problem

Writing explanations for a game or a set of rules

Recording a discussion

Representing information graphically

Going from draft work to a polished written product

Talking

Describing and explaining

Clarifying ideas

Asking and answering questions

Discussing within a group

Making generalisations and predictions

Practical work

Making models

Practical measuring

Organising and sorting apparatus

Collecting information

Modelling mathematics in different ways

Using mental mathematics in both planned and informal situations

Working with number lines, number cards and number grids

Using calculators to solve problems

Representing mathematical relationships with objects and structured materials

Working with computers

Using measuring equipment

General attitudes towards mathematics

Motivation and interest

Creativity and lateral thinking

Perseverance

Confidence

Enjoyment and satisfaction

Social context

Collaborating in a group

Taking turns playing a game

Working equally with a partner

Leading a group

Teaching a friend

Reporting to the class on work done

Sharing resources

EXPECTATIONS

In any class of children there is a spread of attainment in mathematics, and the differences increase as children get older. The learning objective in a class may be for the children to develop an understanding of place value, but the level at which they achieve this will vary considerably from child to child. Nevertheless, you need to be clear about the learning objectives you have for the children, and to ensure that each child makes progress to the best of his or her potential. This means constantly reassessing the children's understanding, and not making assumptions about either their level of understanding or their ability to understand abstract thinking. If we have the highest expectations of children, and we find out as much about their mathematical understanding as we can, we have the opportunity to plan an effective mathematical curriculum for them.

In our expectations of children, we also need to take into account their individual needs and situations. Children who are learning English may understand the mathematics but not be able to express it clearly. Assessments should be sensitive to children's experience, physical condition, gender, and ethnic, cultural and social backgrounds in order to be fair. Probing what children are thinking and being sensitive to their experiences contribute towards making equitable judgements of their learning.

RECORD-KEEPING

A useful motto in record-keeping could be 'Do less, better.' Most record-keeping will be for your own use as a classroom teacher, and this means thinking carefully about what you need the records for. Much of the assessment information you have about children will be in your head, but records are useful for various reasons:

✧ Something significant has happened in a child's learning and you don't want to forget it.

✧ You have noticed a child's misconception in one area of mathematics.

✧ The group of children you were working with came up with some surprises, so you will need to modify your future lesson plans.

✧ You want to make sure you haven't 'forgotten' any children over a certain period of time.

✧ You need to inform others about the children's progress.

Records of your ongoing assessment of children relate directly to planning; so it makes sense to keep planning and assessment records together, and to make sure that the links between them are explicit. One way of doing this is to have a notebook and, as you go along, to 'flip and scribble', focusing *only on new insights*. Another way is to have planning sheets for each session you have planned, on which you can make notes during the lesson. Again, we can use work on place value as an example:

Learning objectives	Activity	Children	Assessment	What next?
Can organise a number of objects into groups of ten and give the total, counting in tens and ones.	How many things in the jar?	Mina Yvonne Marshall Amy Parveen James	Observe how child organises counting.	James: more structure – Unifix cubes and bun tins. Mina, Amy: try hundreds.
Having organised objects as above, can write the total number.			Ask child to write down number.	Yvonne, James: number reversals – check.
When shown a written number, can say how many sets of ten that number of objects would make, and how many objects would be left over.			Show child number written down and ask.	Yvonne, James: more work on grouping.
Can find ways of solving a problem.			Observe how child tackles overall problem.	James: more discussion on how to tackle problems.

You will have decided on the learning intentions and the activity (this could be a standard, photocopied sheet contained in the scheme of work). You record which children have done the activity, any learning objectives *not* covered, any unexpected assessed outcomes, and notes about what needs to be done next. In other words, you don't spend time recording the obvious: only interesting or unusual outcomes that will affect your future plans. Remember, you can't assess all outcomes for all children – so look actively for the unexpected and the significant.

SAMPLING

You could also keep a sample of a child's work, annotated with your comments, if it shows something significant about the child's learning, or if you want to spend time analysing any errors it contains. In terms of assessment, keeping samples of children's work is useful for helping to shape further planning, for analysis and discussion with the children, and as a record of significant achievement. Otherwise, keeping children's work serves the purpose of accountability, which will be a matter of school policy. But generally, it is worth keeping only what is useful and only as much as you can cope with – certainly not everything.

KEEPING TRACK

If you are working with a group, you can make quick notes as you go along. If you are working with a whole class, you could make notes in the same way that involve modifications to your planning, and evidence to support these modifications. If children are working independently, you could select a few in each session to focus on and discuss their work. You need a strategy to make sure that you don't forget 'invisible' children. One teacher, over a four-week period, made sure she knew something about every child. She would spend half an hour a week writing down what she knew about all of the children. At the end of the month, she looked to see which child she'd left out, and made sure she focused on that child the next week.

CHILDREN'S ASSESSMENTS OF THEMSELVES

Older children can be asked to make written comments about the mathematics they do, and make their own assessments of their progress. Marking the child's work can become a dialogue between you and the child, with comments and replies such as 'I liked doing this, and I think I understand it', 'That's great, you've learned about... and now you'll need to learn about...' It is also a time for children to consider 'What have I learned?' and for you to ask 'What do you think you have learned?'

REPORTING

How this is organised will depend on the school's policy. Usually it means summarising children's progress at the end of a term or a year, and keeping samples of work. You need to have evidence available from your ongoing records to support your summary assessment of each child, for the next teacher, the parents, and the next school. Record-keeping shared between teachers involves trust, and you need to ask yourself: 'Can the next teacher pick up from where I left off?'

CONCLUSION

Assessments of children's learning need to be a part of everyday teaching. How these assessments are made, how the evidence is collected, what is done with the evidence and how it is acted on all require careful thought and planning. Planning and assessment should be inextricably linked; and in teaching mathematics, there should be a dynamic cycle of teaching, assessing and modifying plans. Record-keeping should support this process, rather than being a cumbersome activity performed for its own sake. Some mathematical activities are particularly suitable for specific assessments, but all activities should be designed to offer opportunities for probing children's understanding of mathematics.

A teaching style, making use of high-level questions, should be developed that not only elicits information about children's mathematical ideas, but also stimulates and challenges their thinking further. In this way, assessment and teaching can be dynamically related.

CHAPTER 9

CONCLUSION

GETTING ON WITH THE JOB...

At the end of reading a book like this, we inevitably ask ourselves the question: 'So what does this mean we should do, or not do as we get on with the job of trying to raise numerate children and young adults?' What message does this book, taken as a whole, convey?

The book has focused our attention on various aspects of teaching numeracy. The model of classroom number work presented in the Introduction has surfaced, in one or more of its aspects, in each chapter:

Teach	Make sense	Practise

The bulk of the book has been most concerned with the 'teaching' phase of this process, either in terms of *where* we start teaching or in terms of precisely *which* numerical skills should be taught and how. Chapter 2 emphasised that young children's existing knowledge must be an important factor in helping teachers to focus their teaching of number. Chapter 8 reinforced this point with a detailed analysis of how to assess children's numerical knowledge within the context of the busy primary classroom. In Chapters 4 and 5 we considered particular aspects of numeracy, with a focus on algorithms and calculators. In both of these chapters, the stress is upon the precise nature of the skills involved as children produce, develop and recall their own procedures. The differences between written and oral procedures are an important consideration in assessing what the nature and content of the teacher's exposition should be. Chapter 7 focused attention upon the resources that teachers can draw upon as they struggle to help children become numerate. Particular pedagogical resources, such as fingers and the abacus, were discussed both in terms of their history or genesis and in relation to their use as practical numerical tools.

The focus upon pedagogical resources (of various kinds) is one which surfaces in several chapters. In chapter 6, Valerie Emblen described how the diversity of home languages of bilingual or multilingual children can be an enormous resource in terms of the teacher's articulation and explanation of numerical operations and concepts. Chapter 3 suggested that, as mathematics educators and as teachers, we can profitably move away from a notion of children's understanding of mathematics towards a way of thinking which focuses on how children read or interpret mathematical statements. The chapter explored the different types of reading which can be produced by a teacher or a child, and discussed how each reading leads on to the the utilisation or development of particular numerical strategies and techniques.

Teaching numeracy, as this book confirms, is a complex process; it comprises an amalgam of highly technical as well as almost intuitive skills. It is useful to consider these under three headings: context, pedagogy and process.

1. THE CONTEXT OF OUR TEACHING

We need to start with what the children already know. We need to be aware of what they have learned and grappled with beforehand, both inside and outside the school. Finding out where to start in our teaching is partly a professional and technical process and partly an intuitive one. Teachers, unless they are unusually thick-skinned, know when they are teaching either over the children's heads or to children who already know the material. The latter is, in many ways, worse than the former, because the children not only find it boring – and so cease to listen to the teacher even when she is saying something they do not know – but are also mildly insulted!

As Chapter 8 makes clear, there are many ways in which teachers can make themselves aware of the knowledge base of most of the children in the class. It is not simply a matter of time-consuming individual assessments, nor of whole-class tests which are so general as to be almost useless. Also, as the second chapter emphasises, children bring with them a whole world of specifically numerical experience from outside the classroom, and we ignore this at our peril.

So the context we pitch into when we start a particular piece of teaching is all-important; and to some degree, even with the most knowledgeable teacher and the best-planned classroom, we shall be assessing the children's competencies in a topic as we start teaching that topic. Which brings us to the pedagogy.

2. THE PEDAGOGY OF TEACHING NUMERACY

It is clear from the whole focus and tone of this book that we believe that the teacher's 'up-front' teaching role is both active and crucial in the teaching of numeracy. There needs to be some exposition, usually to a large group or the whole class, in which the teacher demonstrates a particular numerical technique in order to provide children with the strategies they need to perform a particular arithmetic operation. Thus the teacher may be demonstrating how to 'count on' in multiples of ten, or how to work out a subtraction by equal addition (e.g. when taking 29 from 45, add 1 to both numbers). These demonstrations will have an element of 'performance' in them – it is not coincidental that many writers have likened some aspects of teaching to acting. The teacher is literally 'modelling' what it is to perform these operations.

This up-front exposition often kicks off a numeracy topic with a large group of children, all of whom are at slightly different levels within the topic, and some of whom may be at a very different stage. The first part of the introduction will frequently be a 'warm-up' activity, where the teacher is able to assess where individual children are coming from and to provide some rehearsal of those pre-requisite skills which are needed at this point. After the exposition, the teacher will need to provide a series of differentiated activities for the children. Some groups will be able to follow the teacher's demonstrations or explanations; by a process of imitation and translation (turning the teacher's words into their own words), they will develop the strategies provided and apply the techniques to carry out the necessary numerical operations. Other children will require an opportunity for further teaching; a small-group activity supervised by the teacher, perhaps focused upon slightly easier examples or special cases of the same operation, will enable these children to get a better grip on the topic being taught. Often, there will also be a group of children who are capable of going on from where the teacher left off, generating more complex examples and a series of new techniques for completing these.

Good teaching in numeracy, as in other areas of the curriculum, also involves recognising the crucial role of repetition and memorisation. Even when children have achieved a basic level of competence in a certain area of numeracy, they need to practice these skills in both written and oral form. This further practise enables children to achieve a degree of automaticity of skill – that is to say, to reach a state where they can perform the operation *without thinking about it*. This is very important when the skills are fairly basic ones, which children will utilise as parts of more complex sets of procedures or algorithms later in their mathematical learning. For example, children need to be able to add and subtract multiples of ten, round numbers up or down to the nearest 10 or 100, and double and halve numbers, without having to think long and hard about it. These skills, and many others, need to be on 'automatic pilot', and it is the element of practice which is of crucial moment here.

3. THE PROCESS OF TEACHING NUMERACY

The process of teaching numeracy to students in real-life classrooms is often fraught with a series of contingent and specific difficulties which the above section might seem to mask or render invisible. In dealing with these, teachers need to encompass the following different stages:

(i) They will enable the children to consider a number of diverse formulations (oral and written) of specific numerical problems. Thus *seventeen add three is twenty* can be formulated in a number of different ways, including:

17 + 3 = ❑ 17 + ❑ = 20 20 – 17 = ❑

Seventeen and something more is twenty.

What do we add to 17 to make 20?

How many more than 17 is 20?

(ii) They will provide a series of appropriate ways in which children can *read the mathematical statements* they encounter. This helps children to know what to do, and to give a mathematical meaning to what they are doing. The important thing here is that the teacher is *providing a vocabulary* in which the children can discuss their work, and which then becomes a resource which the child can draw upon in thinking things through and working them out.
(iii) They can contextualise the different readings of these mathematical statements in such a way as to help the child to interpret and negotiate the mathematical meanings. Thus providing the above-mentioned example as a 'Who has more money?' question will foreground the difference and counting-on aspects, whereas asking 'What is the total of seventeen and three' will highlight the number bonds aspect.

Through an attention to the necessity of providing different formulations and a diversity of contexts, teachers can broaden children's ability to 'read' mathematics. But it is nearly always with the readings provided by the teacher, and with the vocabulary and terminology he or she uses, that the child is compelled to start. Without that resource, it is very difficult to develop any sort of numerical fluency, except on the part of the brightest or most gifted child.

IN CONCLUSION

Finally, then, we are clear that it is the teacher, and how she teaches, that is perhaps the crucial factor in determining how children become numerically fluent.

The teacher needs to have a good overall sense of the child's development in numeracy; a series of benchmarks describing the numerical skills children should have acquired at the end of each school year is a great help here – teachers can produce their own, using the National Curriculum as a guide, or they can look to outside sources.[1] The characterisation and isolation of what may be called 'key skills' is also a real help here. For example, it is difficult to exaggerate the importance of *counting* in all its various guises and formulations. After all, the four arithmetic operations can all be construed in terms of counting: addition as counting *on*, subtraction as counting how many *between* two numbers, multiplication as counting sets and division as counting how many sets in a particular number.

But perhaps the most important aspects of teaching numeracy cannot be covered in a book which, of necessity, focuses on the professional aspects of the task. As many teachers will testify, the most important and rewarding moments in the classroom arise both unexpectedly and unbidden. One such moment occurred for me when, as I was entering a school to do some maths in-service training with the staff, a small child stopped me with the words 'You're the maths person, aren't you?' I confessed to being such a one. He continued, 'Do you want to know something? D'you know that if you start with two and you go right on doubling, eventually you get to one thousand and twenty-four!' As he said this last number, he threw his arms wide to indicate the extent and the size of this magnificent number. I expressed a suitable admiration, and he told me in an offhand manner: 'I learned that in bed!'

NOTES

1. Such a series, consisting of one page for each of Year 1 through to Year 6, can be obtained via the Hamilton Maths Project in Oxford on receipt of a stamped addressed envelope to Hamilton Maths Project, 6 Northmoor Rd, Oxford, OX2 6UP.

BIBLIOGRAPHY

Askew, M., Briscoe, R., Ebbutt, S. and Maple, L. *Number at Key Stage 1* (1994): BEAM.

Askew, M. and Wiliam, D. (1995) *Recent Research in Mathematics Education 5-16*, London: HMSO.

Atkinson, D. & Moore, A. (1994), 'How particular Lacanian notions might be helpful for evaluating profiles of teacher competences and supervising students on their teaching practice' in *Chreods 8* (November 1994) pp. 3–11, Didsbury, Manchester: The Manchester Metropolitan University.

Atkinson, S. (ed.) (1992) *Mathematics with Reason; the emergent approach to primary maths*: Hodder & Stoughton.

Aubrey, C. (1994) *The Role of Subject Knowledge in the Early Years of Schooling*: Falmer Press.

Baratta-Lorton, M. (1976) *Mathematics Their Way*: Addison-Wesley.

Barrett, M. and Trevitt, J. (1991) *Attachment Behaviour and the Schoolchild: an introduction to educational therapy*, London: Routledge.

Behr M, et al (1980) *How Children View the Equals Sign* in *Mathematics Teaching* 92, A.T.M.

Bierhoff, H. (1995) *The Foundations of Numeracy*, London: National Institute of Economic and Social Research.

Bird, M. (1991) *Mathematics for Young Children. An active thinking approach:* Routledge.

Borges, J. L. (1964) 'Funes the Memorious' in *Labyrinths*, London: Penguin.

Brown, T. (1996), 'Narrative and Mathematics' in *Prospero: a journal of new thinking in philosophy for education*, Vol. 2 No. 1 (1996).

Bruner, J (1960) *The Process of Education*: Harvard University Press.

Bruner, J (1975) *Entry into Early Language, A spiral curriculum*: University College of Swansea.

Bruner, J (1986) *Actual Minds, Possible Worlds*: Harvard University Press.

Burns, S. (1994) 'Can we improve teaching and learning?' in Selinger, M. (ed.) *Teaching Mathematics*, London: Routledge & Open University.

Burton, L. (1986) *Girls into maths can go*: Holt Rinehart & Winston.

Burton, L. (1990) *Gender and Maths*: Cassell.

Caspari, I. (1978) *Educational Therapy*, in Varma V. *Psychotherapy Today*, London: Constable.

Checkpoints assessment cards (1980) ILEA, AMS Educational, Leeds.
Clarke, S. and Atkinson, S. (1996) *Tracking Significant Achievement in Mathematics*: Hodder & Stoughton.
Clarke, S. and Brown, A. (1995) *Formative Assessment in KS1 Mathematics*: Hodder & Stoughton.
Clemson, D. and Clemson, W. (1994) *Mathematics in the Early Years*: Routledge.
Cockcroft, W. H. (1982) *Mathematics Counts*, London: HMSO.
Cooper, R. (1989) 'Dwelling and the "therapeutic community"' in *Thresholds: between philosophy and psychoanalysis* (Papers from the Philadelphia Association), London: Free Association Books.
Dahl, R. (1982) *The BFG*, London: Jonathan Cape.
Dawson, S. (1982) *Words Triggered by Images, Images Triggered by Words* in *Mathematics Teaching* 98, A.T.M.
DES (1989) *Mathematics in the National Curriculum*, London: HMSO.
Donaldson, M. (1978) *Children's Minds:* Fontana.
Donaldson, M. (1992) *Human Minds: an exploration*, London: Penguin.
Dörfler, W. (1993) 'Computer use and views of the mind' in C. Keitel and K. Ruthven (eds.) *Learning from Computers: Mathematics Education and Technology*, 159-186, Berlin: Springer-Verlag.
Driver, R. (1983) *The Pupil as a Scientist?*: O.U.P.
Duffin, J. (1993) *Calculators in the Classroom: The reports of the CAN component of the PrIME project, 1987-89 and of the CAN Continuation Project, 1990-92*: Hull University Numeracy Centre.
Ebbutt, S. et al (1994), *A Feel for Number*: BEAM.
Edwards, D. and Mercer, N. (1987) *Common Knowledge, The development of understanding in the classroom*: Methuen.
The Exeter-Cassell Comparative Project, reported in Blum, W., Burghes, D., Green, N. & Kaiser-Messmer, G. (1993) 'British-German Comparative Project: some preliminary results' in *Teaching Mathematics and its Applications*, Vol. 12 No. 1.
Fitzgerald, A. (1985) *New Technology and Mathematics in Employment*: Department of Curriculum Studies, University of Birmingham.
Flavell, J. (1963)*The Developmental Psychology of Jean Piaget*: Van Nostrand.
Foxman, D. (1992) *Learning Mathematics and Science: the Second*

International Assessment of Educational Progress, Slough: NFER.

Friedman, J. (1989) '*Therapeia*, play and the therapeutic household' in *Thresholds: between philosophy and psychoanalysis* (Papers from the Philadelphia Association), London: Free Association Books.

Gatsby Charitable Foundation (1995) *A Review of Research and Demonstration Projects*: The Gatsby Foundation, Red Lion Square, London.

Gattegno, C. (1970) *What We Owe Children: the Subordination of Teaching to Learning*: Routledge & Kegan Paul.

Gattegno, C. (1974) *The Common Sense of Teaching Mathematics*: Routledge & Kegan Paul.

Gattegno, C. (1981) 'Children and Mathematics, A new appraisal' in *Mathematics Teaching* 94, A.T.M.

Gattegno, C. (1983) 'On Algebra' in *Mathematics Teaching* 105, A.T.M.

Gattegno, C. (1987) *The Science of Education: Theoretical considerations pt.1*: Educational Solutions.

Gattegno, C. (1988) *The Science of Education, pt.2b, The awareness of mathematization*: Educational Solutions.

Gifford, S. (1996) *Mathematics in the Primary School: A Sense of Progression*: David Fulton Publishing.

Girling, M. (1977) 'Towards a definition of basic numeracy' in *Mathematics Teaching* 81, pp. 4-5.

Graves, D. (1983) *Writing; Teachers and Children at Work:* Heinemann.

Groves, S. (1994) 'The effect of calculator use on third and fourth graders' computation and choice of calculating device' in J. P. da Ponte and J. F. Matos (eds.) *Proceedings of PME-18* Vol.3: University of Lisbon, pp. 33-41.

Harrison, J. et al 'Young children talking about mathematics' in Mathematics Teaching 144 (Sept. 1993) pp. 6-9.

Heath S. B. (1983) *Ways with Words: Language, Life and Working in Communities and Classrooms*: Cambridge University Press.

Hembree, R. and Dessart, D.J. (1986) 'Effects of hand-held calculators in precollege mathematics: a meta-analysis' in *Journal for Research in Mathematics Education,* 17:2, pp. 83-99.

Hembree, R. and Dessart, D.J. (1992) 'Research on calculators in mathematics education' in Fey, J. and Hirsch, C. (eds.) *Calculators in*

Mathematics Education, Reston VA, National Council of Teachers of Mathematics, pp. 23-33.

Holt, J. (1964) *How Children Fail*, London: Pitman.

Hopkins, C., Gifford, S. and Pepperell, S. (eds.) (1996) *Mathematics in the Primary School: A Sense of Progression*: David Fulton Publishers.

Hughes, M (1981) 'Can Pre-school Children Add and Subtract?' in *Jnl. of Educational Psychology*, 1:3.

Hughes, M (1982) 'Mathematical Thinking in Very Young Children: The origins of written representation': Article based on a talk given to the British Society for the Psychology of Learning Mathematics, at their Manchester Conference.

Hughes, M. (1986) *Children and Number: Difficulties in learning mathematics*: Basil Blackwell.

Inge (Dean), (1917: Ch. 2) 'The training of the reason' in Benson, A. C. (ed.) *Cambridge Essays on Education*: CUP.

Isaacs, N. (1960) *New Light on Children's Ideas of Number: the work of Professor Piaget*: Ward Lock.

Isaacs, N. (1961) *The Growth of Understanding in the Young Child*: Ward Lock.

Kennard, R. (1985) 'Interpreting Fraction Forms' in *Mathematics Teaching* 112, A.T.M.

Lapointe, A.E, Mead, N.A, and Askew, J.M. (1992) *Learning Mathematics*, Princeton NJ: Educational Testing Service.

Lewis, A. (1993) *Starting from Everyday Objects 1: Starting from Calculators*. London: BEAM.

Liebeck, P. (1985) 'Reading Mathematics' in *Mathematics Teaching* 110, A.T.M.

London Mathematical Society (1995) *Tackling the Mathematics Problem*: Report of the London Mathematical Society.

MacLure M. 'The First Five Years' in Norman K. (ed.) *Thinking Voices: The Work of The National Oracy Project*, (1992) Hodder & Stoughton.

Making it Happen: Mathematics in ILEA Primary Schools (1988): AMS Educational.

Mason, J. (1982) 'Attention' in *For the Learning of Mathematics*, 2:3.

Mason, J. H. (1986) 'I is for imagery and imagination' in *The Investigator*, 9:8-9.

Mathematical Association (1992) *Maths Talk* (2nd ed.): the Mathematical Association & Stanley Thornes.

Maths Focus Kit 1 (1996): Scholastic.

McIntosh, A. (1979) 'When Will They Ever Learn?' in Primary Supplement of *Mathematics Teaching* 86, A.T.M.

McIntosh, A., Reys, B. and Reys, R. (1995) 'How old are you?' in *Mathematics Teaching* 153, A.T.M.

Menninger, K. (1969) *Number Words and Number Systems: a Cultural History of Numbers*: MIT.

Merttens, R. and Newland, A. (1996) *Learning in Tandem*: Scholastic.

Munn, P. (1994) 'The Early Development of Literacy and Numeracy Skills' in *European Early Childhood Education Research Jnl.* 2:1.

Murris, K. (1992), *Teaching Philosophy With Picture Books*, Infonet Publications.

Neumark, V. (1996) 'Minds beat fingers hands down' in *Times Educational Supplement*, Maths Extra, 15 March 1996, p. iv.

Non-statutory Guidance: Mathematics in the National Curriculum (1989) NCC, HMSO.

Norman K. (ed.) (1992) *Thinking Voices: The Work of the National Oracy Project*: Hodder & Stoughton.

OFSTED (1994) *Science and Mathematics in Schools: a review*, London: HMSO.

Oram, W. J. (1989) *Some notes on CAN and the Suffolk County Mathematics Test*, Ipswich: Suffolk County Council.

Pea, R.D. (1985) 'Beyond amplification: using the computer to reorganise mental functioning' in *Educational Psychologist* 20, 4, pp. 167-182.

Piaget, J. (1926), *The Language and Thought of the Child*, London: Routledge & Kegan Paul.

Piaget, J. (1952) *The Child's Conception of Number*: Routledge & Kegan Paul.

Piaget, J. (1964) 'Cognitive Development in Children, Development and Learning': Report of proc. of Piaget's address to conference of educators, in *Jnl. of Research in Science Teaching*, 2.

Pimm, D. (1994) 'Another psychology of mathematics education' in Ernest, P. (ed.) *Constructing Mathematical Knowledge: Epistemology and Mathematical Education*, London: Falmer Press.

Pimm D. (1987) *Speaking Mathematically: Communication in Mathematics Classrooms*: Routledge.
Plunkett, S. (1979) 'Icons' in *Mathematics Teaching* 86, A.T.M.
Plunkett, S. (1983) 'Repressed Images' in *Mathematics Teaching* 103, A.T.M.
Prais, S. (1995) *see* Gatsby Charitable Foundation (1995).
Purkey W. (1970) *Self-Concept and School Achievement*, London: Paul Chapman.
Reid, A. (1996) 'Children and rods' (Private correspondence with author).
Rotman, B. (1985) 'On Zero' in *Mathematics Teaching* 113, A.T.M.
Rousham, L. (1995) 'CAN calculators make a difference?' in Anghileri, J. (ed.) *Children's Mathematical Thinking in The Primary Years: Perspectives on Children's Learning*, London: Cassell.
Rowland, T. (1990) 'Apparatus for Number Work' in *CAN Newsletter* 2, Cambridge: CAN Continuation Project, pp. 1-2.
Rowland, T. (1994) *CAN in Suffolk – The Beginnings of a Calculator-Aware Number Curriculum in Three Suffolk Schools*: Homerton Research Report Series, Publication Unit, Homerton College, Cambridge.
Runnymede Trust (1993) *Equality Assurance in Schools*: Trentham Books.
Saunders, K. (1977) 'Measurement: Extracts from an M.Ed. thesis' in *Recognitions* 8, A.T.M.
SCDC (1986) *PrIME Newsletter* 1, London: SCDC Publications.
School Curriculum and Assessment Authority (1995) *Consistency in Teacher Assessment. Exemplification of Standards in Mathematics: Key Stages 1 and 2, Levels 1 to 5*: School Curriculum and Assessment Authority.
Shuard, H., Walsh, A., Goodwin, J. and Worcester, V. (1991) *Calculators, Children and Mathematics*, London: Simon & Schuster.
Siraj-Blatchford, I. (1994) *The Early Years: Laying the Foundations of Racial Equality*: Trentham Books.
Skemp, R. (1971) *The Psychology of Learning Mathematics*: Penguin Books.
Skuttnab-Kangas, T. and Cummins, J. (1988) *Minority Education, From Shame to Struggle*, Clevedon Philadelphia: Multilingual Matters Ltd.
Spencer (1982) *Narrative Truth and Historical Truth*: Norton.
Stern, C. (1953) *Children Discover Arithmetic: an introduction to structural arithmetic*: Harrap.
Straker, A. (1993) *Talking Points in Mathematics*: Cambridge University Press.

Suschitzky W. 'It's not fair! Equal Opportunities in Practice' in Mayles J. (1995) *Beginning Teaching: Beginning Learning in Primary Education*: Open University Press.

Tizard B. and Hughes M. (1984) *Young Children Learning: Talking and Thinking at Home and at School*: Fontana.

TIMSS Reports (1996): International Association for the Evaluation of Educational Achievement (IEA).

Tripp, D. (1993) *Critical Incidents in Teaching*: Routledge.

Van Den Brink, J. (1984) 'Acoustic Counting and Quantity Counting' in *For the Learning of Mathematics*, 4:2.

Vygotsky, L. (1962) *Thought and Language*: MIT Press.

Vygotsky, L. (1978) *Mind and Society, The development of higher psychological processes*: Harvard University Press.

Walden, R. & Walkerdine, V. et al (1985) *Girls and Maths: from primary to secondary schooling*, Bedford Way Papers 024: Institute of Education, University of London.

Walkerdine, V. (1981) *Practice of Reason, pt. 1, Reading the signs of mathematics*: unpublished mimeograph, Institute of Education, London University.

Walkerdine, V. (1982) 'From Context to Text: a psychosemiotic approach to abstract thought' in M. Beveridge (ed.) *Children Thinking Through Language*: Arnold.

Walkerdine, V. (1984) 'Developmental Psychology and the Child-centered Pedagogy: the insertion of Piaget into early education' in J. Henriques, et al (ed.) *Changing the Subject*: Methuen.

Walkerdine, V. (1988) *The Mastery of Reason, Cognitive development and the production of rationality*: Routledge.

Walkerdine, V. (1989) *Counting Girls Out*: Virago.

Warren, V. and Ling, J.G. (1994) 'Calculators in the primary school since the introduction of the National Curriculum' in *Mathematics Education Review* 4, pp. 30-40.

Weyl-Kailey (1985) *Victoires sur les maths: comprendre les causes de l'echec et rehabiliter les nuis en maths*, Paris: Robert Laffont.

Williams, H. (1989) *Tuning in to Young Children, An exploration of contexts for learning mathematics*: Unpublished MPhil. thesis, Open University.

Williams, H. 'Beginning Beginnings' in *Mathematics Teaching* 156, (Sept.

1996) pp. 8-13: A.T.M.

Winnicott, D. W. (1971) *Playing and Reality*, Tavistock, Harmondsworth: Penguin 1974 ed.

Winnicott, D. W. (1986: p55-56) '*Sum*, I Am': a talk given to the Association for Teachers of Mathematics, Easter Conference, London, April 1968, published in Winnicott, D. W. *Home is where we start from*, London: Penguin.

Wood, D. (1988) *How Children Think and Learn*: Blackwell.

INDEX